THE LIVE LECKY

To the memory of Winnie, Frank and Mary Cowhig.

ACKNOWLEDGEMENTS

I would like to thank the following people:
John Kennedy: for his many helpful suggestions and contributions.
Paul Fallon: four his eagel-eyed proof-reading.
Ian Boumphrey: for his help with publication and distribution.
Merseyside Comedy Writers: for their support and encouragement.
Pauline and Imelda: for tolerating all the late nights
(when they thought we were working on the book).
The people of Liverpool: for providing the raw material for the stories.
Lee Burns: for all the art work.
And especially **Jim Toal** for his invaluable help in writing the book.

All the events in this book took place before Manweb was privatised in 1990.

Some names and places have been changed to protect anonymity.

Origination
Ian Boumphrey – Desk Top Publisher

Printed by:
Bootle Printing Company, Phone & Fax 0151 922 8566

Contents

FOREWORD

'Liverpool is a two-fisted, broken-nose town with a heart of gold'

This was how my city was described in a documentary on The Beatles some years ago. I might have added that Liverpool is also a city of art and culture, but I couldn't argue. I have lived here all my life and know that Liverpool is, and always will be, *a two-fisted, broken-nose town with a heart of gold*.

For twenty-six years I was employed by the electricity board and during that time I must have called on nearly 80,000 houses in and around this great city. In every one there was a story to be told – some happy, some sad and some just plain crazy.

I started as a meter collector for Manweb in May 1968 when ten shilling notes, half-crowns and pennies were still part of our currency. Electricity was paid for by means of a slot meter and the rate at which it was charged could be varied. As electricity was burned, the speed of the timer would determine how much money had to be put in. When the meter required more money, the supply would cut out. This usually occurred at a crucial moment – as the centre-forward was poised to score in the last minute of the cup final or when the inspector was about to reveal who murdered the bishop. When this happened, often the TV got murdered as well.

In those days most people didn't have bank accounts, so a lot of householders used their meters as 'piggy banks' and chose to have the timer set at a faster rate than necessary. If the standard rate was, say, tuppence a unit, they would pay sixpence. The meter was emptied every three months and the customer would then get a very handsome rebate. This was known as a 'divvy', short for 'dividend'. Thirty years ago the divvy meant short-lived wealth.

The 1974 world oil crisis put an end to the divvy. Up to that time, electricity had been heavily subsidised by the government but, after the dramatic rise in oil prices, the subsidy disappeared and, consequently, so did the rebates. Sadly, the generous tips the collectors used to receive began to disappear too.

However, when the divvy was at its height, we were the most important people in the community. A divvy could sometimes be the equivalent of a fortnight's wages and the people of Liverpool were suitably appreciative.

'Do you want a cup of tea, lad?'

'Do you fancy a whisky?'

'Would you like to stay for your dinner?'

'Do you want to come upstairs?'

I am sworn to secrecy as to which collectors accepted which offers.

Being out when the collector called was seen as a major tragedy. When we were due in a particular area, we would often see groups of small children posted as lookouts. The first one to spot the collector would get sixpence. We were known to all as 'The Lecky Man' and as we came into view, the street would be abuzz.

'Here's the Lecky Man! Here's the Lecky Man!' We would hear this excited chorus every day.

Nothing was allowed to disturb the collector at work. As a child myself I can remember sitting with my cousins in my grandmother's parlour, not daring to breathe as the collector was counting the money from her meter.

My gran used to terrify us. 'If you make one move while the man's counting, he'll put you in his bag and take you away with him!' We never moved a muscle. Years later I often watched children frozen to the spot by the same words. I still sometimes wonder how much bed-wetting this caused.

A lot of children were fascinated watching the Lecky Man counting and stacking the piles of coins. They would tell us what they would buy if the money were theirs.

'If that was my money I'd buy a sweet shop!'

'I'd buy an ice-cream van and go on me holidays in it!'

'I'd buy a helicopter and go to heaven to see me gran!'

I remember one little girl with her nose on the table looking through a stack of coins. I asked her what she could see. 'A little city,' she replied. In her mind the money columns had turned into skyscrapers separated by little narrow streets full of tiny people.

Many wives did not tell their husbands how much they got back in the divvy.

'If he found out how much I've got,' one woman told me, 'he'd stop it out of my housekeeping.' She then urged me to count it as quickly as I could, because she was expecting him home any minute. Have you ever seen one of those movies when the bomb squad are trying to defuse a bomb? Time is rapidly running out. Which wire should they cut – the blue or the red? Sweat trickles down their faces as they hover with the cutters. The tension is unbearable... I've experienced the same feeling trying to count fifty pounds in two-shilling pieces while half-expecting the husband to walk in and start World War III.

Back in 1968, collectors rarely visited the same house twice. Later, following an extensive (and expensive) psychological study, we were all given regular rounds in an effort to promote good customer relations.

This didn't last though it was popular with customers, benefiting them in a way management hadn't foreseen. If we knew them well and they needed cash urgently, we would deliberately read the meter incorrectly. For example, if 1000 units had been used at a cost of £20 and there was £50 in the meter, then the customer would get £30 divvy. However, if the figure was misread as 500 units, then the divvy would be topped up to £40. Head Office would put this down to the collector's carelessness and the customer would have to pay back the difference on the next call. In this way we were able to help people whom we liked and trusted. In return,

4

grateful customers would invite us to all sorts of functions: weddings, engagement parties, twenty-firsts, even funerals.

Some desperate people couldn't wait for the collector to call so they helped themselves to the contents of the meter. When we called, there were all sorts of excuses as to why the meter lock was missing.

'The telly's on the blink an yer 'ave to bang it dead 'ard. That's when the lock fell off!'

'We've got rats!'

'The baby fell down the stairs and banged his head on the lecky cupboard!'

There was no shortage of explanations for the absent lock, but it was a mystery how the money found its way to the pub or the local bookmaker.

In the early eighties burglaries became a serious problem. Thieves would follow us on our rounds and were soon able to work out when the meters of different streets were due to be emptied. They would then break into houses a day or two beforehand and do the job for us. The customer was always responsible for the money in the meter and having to make up the loss could be hard to bear. There was rough justice meted (not to say metered) out to those thieves who were caught red-handed.

Surprises always lurked ready to ambush the unsuspecting collector. I was once standing outside a block of high-rise flats when a TV landed right beside me, exploding like a mortar shell and peppering me with fragments of glass and plastic. I must have jumped six feet in the air with fright. Police later visited a man on the sixteenth floor whose four-horse accumulator had failed by the shortest of short heads.

Despite such incidents, team spirit amongst the collectors was always high. We were like a company of foot soldiers constantly regrouping to check for casualties.

Now, of course, everything is far more efficient. Direct debits, standing orders, electronic payment cards have made the old collectors obsolete. It's progress of a sort, I suppose, but I can't help feeling sad at the ending of an era.

This book is an attempt to keep its memory alive. These stories are not about me or slot meters. We were only innocent bystanders. They are about the people of Liverpool and I hope they convey the colour and flavour of this great city.

Someone once said that Liverpool was full of comedians. Then someone else replied you had to be a comedian to live there. All I know is that I have laughed for twenty six-years of my working life in this *two-fisted, broken-nose town with a heart of gold*. Given the chance, I would do it all over again.

Dave Cowhig 1999

MANWEB staff letting their hair down at the 1974 Christmas party. The author is in the middle of the back row grinning inanely.

6

TOMMY AND THE MONKEY

When I started working for Manweb, our foreman, Tommy Greenwood, was based at the famous Derby House in Liverpool city centre. The big disappointment in Tommy's life was the end of the Second World War. However, he did derive great comfort from knowing that twenty feet below his office, through reinforced concrete, were the wartime tactical headquarters of the Battle of the Atlantic.

Tommy had fought in the Far East during the war and never missed an opportunity to speak of the hardships he had to endure.

'Yes, I was there,' he would say. 'You could live on raw snake and tell how old an elephant was just by smelling its dung. Yes, I was there, you know!'

Tommy was five foot three and built like the proverbial brick outhouse, but otherwise he could have passed for George Formby's twin brother. He had big ears, buckteeth and greased-back hair. All he lacked was a ukulele.

We were often tempted to ask him if things had 'turned out nice again' but we never did. Since he claimed to have once killed two enemy soldiers single-handed in the jungle, we didn't think it wise to provoke him.

In a funny way I always felt sorry for those two soldiers. If you're going to get killed by anyone in war, then make sure he's six foot two, broad-shouldered and kicks arse, and for good measure he should also have blue eyes, a square jaw and be a mate of Kelly's Heroes. For your own self-respect, it's vital that your killer should look the part. Tommy didn't, but still we took no chances. We always left the room backwards.

Of course he was an expert in survival techniques. 'Oh yes, I was dropped behind enemy lines with me donkey and enough food for a week. After that, the jungle floor was your dinner table.'

We were never quite sure how true Tommy's war exploits were. I often wondered if the British Army really did have a Donkey Parachute Regiment!

None of the collectors ever lived up to Tommy's expectations. We were all complete failures. 'You lot would never have got through basic training!' he constantly used to tell us.

Whatever the city of Liverpool could fling at us – bricks, bottles, TVs, dead cats – it never compared to anything that Tommy experienced during the war. However, little did we know that Tommy's jungle skills were soon to be put to the sternest test.

For two years the collectors had had a running battle with a small monkey called Harry. This monkey lived with a mad Irish woman called Bridget Mullen in an old rambling house on Low Hill in Everton. No matter what you did, the monkey would always attack you without warning. What made it worse was Mrs Mullen's attitude.

'It's alright, he's only playing,' she always insisted. Only playing! I would sooner turn my back on Tommy than the monkey. Even with Tommy's much vaunted record, you still stood a better chance of survival.

Mind you, I was lucky. The one time I called at Mrs Mullen's she was out.

The other collectors were not so fortunate.

Ace was the first casualty. The monkey jumped across the table and took a large chunk out of his ear lobe.

Big Ron thought he had escaped the monkey's wrath, but no. As he was about to step into the street, Harry dropped upside down from the fanlight, pulled off Ron's glasses and gouged a three-inch furrow in his cheek.

Mogsy was bending down by the meter cupboard when the monkey spotted his cleavage peeping invitingly above his trousers. When he returned to the office, he had a very pained expression on his face. To this day he has never told anyone exactly what the monkey did.

The Silver Fox got off quite lightly. He'd just finished working out Mrs Mullen's bill when Harry grabbed all the paperwork and threw it into the fire. He then jumped up onto the table and scattered all the money that had just been stacked and counted.

Poor old Armpit was bitten in the groin. Well, it was originally his knee but he always exaggerated and, as the weeks went by, the bite moved further and further up his leg.

Tommy was never sympathetic. 'God! I don't know why I listen to you lot! It's only a little monkey having a bit of fun.' And then he would go into 'the most poisonous snake in the jungle was me best mate' routine. (This always puzzled me – what happened to his donkey?) 'It's fear that lets you down. Once you show fear, the monkey knows you're vulnerable.' He would drone on and on. 'If you lot had been in the jungle, you wouldn't have lasted five minutes. The jungle would have smelled your fear and eaten you alive. From your toes up and your head down. Then Japanny wallah... many... jig... jig... jig!' I never knew what this meant but he would stick an imaginary bayonet in your stomach, salivating as he twisted it in and out.

I'm not sure if Tommy was ever diagnosed as having malaria but we certainly thought he had dementia.

There was no point in ever complaining to Tommy about anything. If you showed him your wounds, he would go one better and drop his trousers. Running from his groin down past his right knee was a huge, ugly scar.

'Some chancer jumped me from behind. Me mate, Eddie Fogg, finished the bugger off, but not before he carved his name on me leg with his bayonet!'

One night, after Tommy had gone, we called a union meeting. The monkey was the first item on the agenda. Mogsy proposed that Mrs Mullen and The Monkey of

Low Hill, Everton should be permanently blacked by the collectors. There was no need for debate.

'All those in favour raise your hands,' said the shop steward, Red Lenny. Twenty-five hands out of twenty-five went up. 'Right brothers, the decision is unanimous.' That was the easy bit. The hard bit was telling Tommy. He was not impressed.

'To think I spilled my blood in the defence of democracy, just so you pathetic bunch of cowards could victimise a poor old woman and a dumb animal. God, you make me sick!' He opened his drawer and we all ducked in anticipation of a hail of bullets. When he stood up, he was holding a bottle of whisky.

As the days passed, Tommy's displeasure grew and his insults had a sharper edge. However, the rank and file of the GMBU (Collectors' Division) stood firm. We all knew the day would come when Mrs Mullen's meter would need emptying.

That day finally arrived one Friday morning. An angry Mrs Mullen called at Derby House and demanded that someone should come and empty her meter. The box was full and she had no electricity.

Tommy sat her down in his office and gave her a cup of tea. 'None of them had to fight during the war. They don't know what hardship is.' He deliberately left the door open so that we could hear. 'You see, I fought in the Far East, so I'm used to jungle animals.'

Tommy told Mrs Mullen not to worry and promised that he would empty her meter personally that very same day. She went away mollified.

After lunch, Tommy checked his uniform in the mirror and straightened his Manweb cap. 'Look at the creases in these trousers,' he said proudly. 'You could cut your fingers on them.' He did indeed look immaculate as he set off.

When I got back from my afternoon round, Tommy's desk was empty. I half-expected him to jump out of the cupboard with his bayonet, but there was no sign of him. The rest of the lads started to drift back, all asking the same question: 'Where's Tommy?'

At five o'clock we began to get worried. Alright, he was an awkward bastard but he was a colleague and he had defended democracy during the war. He also had the keys to the safe where our wages were.

Mogsy, Big Ron and myself decided to call on Mrs Mullen. Her house, like its owner, had seen better days. The painted brickwork, which had once been white, was now yellow with age. Ron and I stood behind Mogsy as he knocked nervously on the door. Instantly, the curtains lifted and there stood the monkey on the window sill.

'That monkey looks like he's laughing at us,' Ron said, and it was true. He really did seem to be laughing, baring his teeth as he turned circles and banged hard on the window pane.

Mrs Mullen opened the door. We all braced ourselves in case the monkey decided to attack us, but fortunately he'd been locked in the front room.

Ron was our spokesman. 'Sorry to bother you, Mrs Mullen, but did Mr Greenwood from Manweb call to empty your meter?'

'God love him, he's a nice man, Mr Greenwood. The ambulance man said he'd probably be alright.'

We exchanged glances. 'Why, what happened?' asked Ron, thinking mostly about his wages.

'Well, at first he was getting on fine with Harry. They was playing games and Mr Greenwood told me all about his time in the Far East.' This had the ring of truth about it. 'You lads know what Harry's like, God bless him!' She shook her head indulgently.

We could barely control our impatience, but there was no hurrying her. Mogsy was glaring at the monkey who was now gesticulating at us through the window.

'You little rascal!' Mrs Mullen looked affectionately at her pet. 'What did you go and do that for, you silly old boy?' She smiled at the monkey, then turned her attention back to us. 'Jumped on Mr Greenwood's head, did Harry, the little devil! Did a number two right down his neck.'

So! The monkey had had the temerity to shit upon the great Tommy Greenwood, late of the Far East and war hero. Clearly he was no respecter of status.

'Then he sat on his shoulder and did a number one in his face. Good thing Mr Greenwood had already emptied the meter.' She went to shut the door but my foot was in the way.

'Hang on a minute! Why did you need to call an ambulance?' I could appreciate Tommy's discomfort but I couldn't see what good a doctor would have done. Anyway, wouldn't he have suffered similar indignities in the jungle?

'Oh, he banged his head when he fainted. They've taken him down to the Infirmary.' She didn't look particularly upset as she closed the door in our faces.

'Better get down there, I suppose,' said Ron. 'We can walk it in ten minutes.' As I turned to take one last look at the monkey, he shoved his backside against the window in farewell. Had someone handed me a brick I don't think I would have missed.

Finding Tommy in Casualty was easy. As we walked in we heard a nurse's voice. 'Come with me, Mrs Greenwood. You can see your husband now.'

A large, imposing lady rose from her chair and sailed imperiously down the corridor. She was wearing a bold wide-brimmed hat, of a similar colour to Mrs Mullen's brickwork, and her backside resembled the leading jockey's bottom in the overweight Grand National. (Had someone handed me a brick I definitely wouldn't have missed!) They stopped outside a cubicle.

'He's had a nasty bang on his head,' explained the nurse, 'so he may be a bit confused.'

Mrs Greenwood seemed unconcerned. 'He's been confused for the last twenty-odd years. I don't suppose I'll notice any difference.' She disappeared behind a curtain.

We hovered around until the nurse had gone, then went and stood outside. Ron wanted to sneak in and get the keys to the safe and Mogsy and I had to restrain him.

'What the bloody hell have you been up to?' Mrs Greenwood's voice bristled with scorn.

'I was attacked by a bloody great gorilla. Huge he was! Had to call on all me old fighting skills.'

'You're the one who's a bloody great gorilla! The war's been over twenty-five years, Tommy. It's about time you grew up!' Outside we struggled desperately to contain our laughter.

'Have you got me clothes with you?' asked the jungle hero plaintively. 'The nurse has bagged up me uniform.'

'There's an old jumper and your gardening trousers. You'll have to make do with them. And don't think you're coming into my house stinking like that.' By now the smell had started to spread into the corridor. 'Go up to Margaret Street Baths! You can use their soap and towel.' I knew Tommy had met his wife during the war. Now I knew how. She must have been his Regimental Sergeant Major.

'Can't I use our bath? Me head's really sore.' Tommy sounded just like a little kid.

'No!' Mrs Greenwood was uncompromising. 'I cleaned it out this morning and I'm not having you messing it up again!' Beside me Mogsy was having silent hysterics.

'Can I help you, gentlemen?' The nurse materialised suddenly behind us.

'Oh, er... we came to see Mr Greenwood, but his wife's in with him. We didn't like to disturb them. We're just leaving now.' The nurse watched us suspiciously as we made our way back to the waiting-room.

Magazines prudently concealed our faces when Tommy and the sergeant-major finally emerged. We felt that now wasn't the best time to bring up the matter of our wages. As he shuffled past, everyone looked round to see where the smell was coming from.

Outside, Tommy trudged along behind his wife, a forlorn figure, head bandaged and bent, shoulders slumped, his immaculate uniform soiled and crumpled in a plastic bag. This was one day that definitely hadn't 'turned out nice again'. Within a couple of hours Tommy had lost his war, beaten not by enemy soldiers, but by a little monkey and a member of the 'weaker sex'.

For the next few weeks there was a strong smell of aftershave in Tommy's office. And things just weren't the same. There were no boasts, no insults, no mention of the war at all. Tommy was all sweetness and light and it was unnerving.

Then one day, many months later, the war hero returned. Big Ron was bitten by a ferret. No sooner had he walked into Tommy's office to show him his injury than

Tommy dropped his trousers.

'I was there, you know,' he said, 'deep in the heart of the jungle. Yes, I was one of the few.'

Two years later there was a sad sequel to this story. Apparently the monkey often slept in Mrs Mullen's washing basket, curled up in one of her sheets. While she was out, her sister, who was visiting from Ireland, bundled the washing into the machine and put it on a hot wash. Mrs Mullen's screams when she discovered Harry's sodden remains could be heard from miles away.

The story, though, didn't end there. Mrs Mullen had Harry stuffed and placed on the mantelpiece. One day Mogsy was emptying her meter when he screamed and ran out in terror. He swore afterwards that he had seen the monkey move. I, for one, would not have been surprised if he had.

SICK AS A PARROT

It has always amazed me how parrots can mimic the sound of the human voice. I remember one in particular that had a talent Mike Yarwood would have envied. This parrot lived in a small terraced house just off West Derby Road, near the centre of Liverpool.

Mrs Lily Pike opened the door and, without pausing for breath, said how pleased she was to see me.

'Thank God, I didn't miss you... I had to nip out to the shops and then go to the post office for me pension and I wouldn't mind but the bloody meter's full and I've been out of me mind with worry about all the break-ins we've had and anyway the meter's in the front room but if you don't mind you can count the money in the back 'cause it's a bit warmer in there. Anyway, come in lad, come in!'

One thing I've learned over the years is, when you get a gabbler, switch off. Otherwise you get sucked into a world of *'Well, the doctor's never seen a rash like it'*, *'Oh, they should bring back hanging, I say'* or *'She's had six different kids to six different men, she's just a trollop, if you ask me'*. I never did ask and did my best to keep such ramblings to a minimum.

I unlocked the meter and took the box through into the back room where a grey parrot with a red tail sat in a cage by the window. Mrs Pike started gabbling to me again.

'That bird's still pining for me husband 'cause parrots often form a very close bond with one person, you know, and we've had him since 1945 which is why we called him Monty after the Field-Marshal so he's nearly thirty now but they do say that it's not unusual for African Greys like Monty to live for anything up to sixty years or even longer which means he's still quite young really and I know of one that lived till it was eighty. So, who's a pretty boy then?' I guessed the last remark was addressed to the parrot.

Mrs Pike poured me a cup of tea while I sat at the table to count the money. Thankfully, by now she'd stopped talking. She didn't want to put me off my 'reckoning' as she called it.

The noise of the money clanging out of the metal box must have startled the parrot. He suddenly began to cough, not just a sharp cough but a long chesty cough, followed by a bout of retching and spitting, then the sound of phlegm hitting the bucket. I didn't think this one was likely to make it to sixty.

As the parrot went quiet, I turned to Mrs Pike. 'I think he needs to see a vet.'

Mrs Pike shook her head. 'No, the parrot's not sick. That was me husband when he was dying, God bless him!'

The parrot listened to our conversation and treated us to a repeat performance. This time a man's voice could be heard saying, 'God help me!' It was followed by a loud fart.

Mrs Pike looked at me. 'All the medicines he was on gave him wind,' she explained.

I soon learned that Albert and Lily Pike had been married for thirty-five years when Albert died. He smoked sixty cigarettes a day, despite suffering badly with asthma.

'Albert always had a good cough after a ciggy,' she insisted. 'It helped him clear his chest.' I said nothing. I suppose it takes all sorts to make a world.

Despite his 'medicinal' cigarettes, Albert had taken to his bed two years ago with a serious lung complaint. The last six months of his life were spent in the back room. Lily had become worn out walking up and down the stairs every five minutes, so she brought the single bed down for him. This also suited Albert as it meant he could be close to his beloved parrot.

By now the parrot had begun to make sucking noises. Lily's voice went quiet. 'That's Albert on the oxygen.' Another fit of coughing followed and more phlegm hit the bucket.

Monty was re-enacting Albert Pike's death, which I found morbid but fascinating. I asked Lily if this upset her. After all, it was a painful reminder of her husband's last months.

'No, in some ways it's like still having Albert with me,' she said with a sad little smile.

Suddenly, the parrot began to buzz like a swarm of bees in flight. Every so often he would stop and let rip with a salvo of farts.

Mrs Pike could see I was confused. 'The men from the Knights of St Columba would come to say the rosary.' This explained the buzzing. It was the sound of men repeating prayers literally parrot-fashion. 'Albert wasn't religious but they were very good to him. Three times a week they would come. I suppose they meant well.'

The parrot then went into a very bad bout of coughing, spitting and *God help me's*, with more extended farting. He followed this with a long, loud gasp and a crashing thump.

'That's how he died,' explained Lily. 'Fell out of bed and went, just like that.' She took out a hanky and wiped her eyes.

'I'm sorry, Mrs Pike,' I found myself saying. 'If there's anything I can do...' What was I saying? Albert had been dead over a year and a half. Suddenly the parrot started to sing the theme song from *Double Your Money*.

Lily's face lit up. 'Aah! That used to be Albert's favourite programme.'

The mood in the room lightened though Lily said there were times when she could wring Monty's neck. 'Every couple of weeks I have to change the doorbell. You get fed up opening the front door and finding no-one there and I've had to stop using the timer on the oven. I'm sick of taking half-cooked meals out of it.'

Lily said that even her grandchildren got annoyed with the parrot. They would hear the ice cream van in the street, but when they opened the front door it was nowhere to be seen. Monty could learn to mimic any sound very quickly.

As I went back to replace the box on the meter, I heard the front door open and a woman's voice calling up the hall, 'Are you there, Lily?'

I thought the parrot was up to his old tricks until I turned round to be confronted by a large, stern-looking lady. 'What are you doing in this house?' she demanded suspiciously.

Before I had a chance to answer, Lily's voice came from the back room. 'It's the

Lecky Man. He's come to empty the meter.'

The large lady was Lily's sister, Agnes. I followed her into the back room but, to my surprise, Lily wasn't there. She was hanging out her washing in the yard. I was puzzled for a moment until I realised it was Monty's voice I'd heard. I was mightily impressed. Most parrots are good mimics, but you could hold a meaningful conversation with this one.

As Agnes flopped down in the chair, Albert's wheezing tones called a cheery greeting. 'I see fat arse is back.' This was accompanied by the loudest fart yet.

'Shut up, you stupid pillock!' replied Agnes, responding in kind.

At this point Lily came in from the yard and was surprised to see her sister. 'Hello, Agnes. How long have you been here?'

Before she could answer, 'Albert' interrupted. 'Make us a nice cup of tea, love!'

Without thinking, Lily picked up the teapot and walked into the kitchen.

'I've finished now, Mrs Pike.' I called, 'so I'll be off.'

It was 'Albert' who answered. 'You'll have to shout. She's a bit deaf.'

'You go,' Agnes said to me, looking at the parrot balefully. 'I'll tell her you said goodbye.'

As I walked down the hall, I could hear 'Albert' dropping her the broadest of hints. 'Isn't it about time you went?'

Her reply was even blunter. 'One of these days I'm going to toss a tom cat in that cage, you stupid git!'

When I got to the front door Albert... Monty... whoever... called after me, 'Take care of yourself, mate, and have one for me.' Another fart wafted out into the atmosphere.

Once outside I walked a few yards, stopped and looked back thoughtfully. Was it possible that Albert's spirit could have passed into Monty or was this the most intelligent parrot in the world?

A few doors away from Mrs Pike's, I sat in the front room of my next call. As I was counting the cash out of the meter, a car alarm went off in the street outside.

'Is that your car?' asked the lady of the house looking out of the window.

She looked at me very strangely when I replied without thinking:

'I shouldn't worry about it. It's probably the parrot.'

HITTING THE RIGHT NOTE

Mozart's *Clarinet Concerto* is amongst my favourite classical pieces and for many music lovers the second movement is one of the most beautiful ever written. It has a slow, hypnotic quality that lingers in the mind for hours. However, the quality of this piece was lost on the ears of one drunken father I met and the rare talent that performed it was probably lost to the world.

The Tower Hill housing estate on the outskirts of Kirkby accommodated the overspill from a slum clearance programme that ran out of ideas. As was the fashion in the sixties, the estate was built in the middle of nowhere and promptly forgotten. It always reminded me of a prison camp. Even the house numbers had a 'Stalag' feel about them: A26, A27, A28. The first time I went there, I thought I might be co-opted onto the escape committee.

I stood outside A29 and looked in disgust at the rubbish strewn everywhere. An old Ford Escort was slowly sinking into a mud flat that was once a garden, and toys lay all around, smashed and forgotten.

Through a large crack in the front door, I could see up the hall into the living room at the back of the house where a man and a woman appeared to be dancing to the loud disco music which I'd heard from halfway down the street. A little girl, about five years old, opened the front door and ran past me into the garden.

I called up the hall. 'Lecky Man! I've come to empty your meter.' Then I noticed the couple weren't dancing but were slap-bang in the middle of a boxing match. The woman's right eye was badly swollen, suggesting she may have been behind on points. She shoved her husband onto the settee and strode towards me. I quickly took a couple of steps backwards.

'The bastard's been out drinking all night,' she said, leading me into the kitchen. As she bent down to open the meter cupboard, several empty whisky bottles fell out around her feet. She ignored them. 'Count the money on the table there and give us a shout if the kids bother yer. I'll 'ave to go and sort 'im out.'

She was probably only in her early thirties yet she looked fifty. Dark roots had long overtaken her blonde rinse and scars from earlier fights made her look more like Bodell than Bo Derek. As she went out, I asked her if she could turn down the radio.

The clinking of the coins brought two other children to the kitchen. They looked about three years old and were probably twins. Both were totally naked, their bodies sticky and thick with grime. The little girl who had opened the door pushed past them and climbed onto a worktop to watch me count the money. She was followed by another girl, about ten, playing a recorder. For the next five minutes, she played a variety of tunes she had learned in school, including my own favourite, *Colours of Day.*

Meanwhile the fight in the living room had resumed. By the painful sound of her husband's grunts, the woman was staging a comeback.

The five-year-old was fidgeting around on the worktop when she knocked the radio onto a classical music station. The second movement of Mozart's *Clarinet Concerto* was just beginning and I listened contentedly as I counted and stacked the coins. The children watched me, hypnotised. When the movement finished, the twins ran out into the hall. The five-year-old switched off the radio and ran after them.

I picked up the money box and walked back towards the cupboard. As I bent down to replace the box under the meter, Mozart's second movement began again. Puzzled, I turned around and couldn't believe what I was hearing – the ten-year-old was playing the movement perfectly. She played about a quarter of it, then stopped. 'I can't remember the rest,' she said.

I applauded her generously and smiled. 'It must have taken you ages to learn that.'

She shook her head. 'That's the first time I've heard it.'

I didn't believe her. 'You remembered all the notes just like that?'

She seemed quite pleased and smiled shyly. 'I'll play some more if you want.' She went on to amaze me with a selection of Bach, Puccini, Vivaldi and some more Mozart. She even threw in a bit of Acker Bilk. Every tune was perfect.

I stood dumbfounded. 'They must be very impressed with you in school,' I said finally.

'Oh, I don't play them tunes in school. They don't know about them. I only play the school tunes.' She started to play *Colours of Day* again.

'You don't play those tunes in school? But you should. They're wonderful. You must tell your teacher. Where did you learn them?'

She stopped playing. 'I hear some on the telly and get some off the tranny.'

'What programmes do you listen to?' I was fascinated.

'Adverts mostly. I remember the tune, then I figure out where to put me fingers on the recorder. Sometimes I find a station on the tranny playing nice tunes but I have to wait till me mam and dad are out. She began to play a snatch from Dvorak's *New World* Symphony, the tune from the famous Hovis advert.

Meanwhile the fight in the front room was finally coming to an end. The woman appeared in the doorway, rubbing the knuckles of her right hand. Her triumphant expression revealed she had just landed the winning blow. I was about to tell her what a gifted daughter she had, but I never got the chance.

'Who left the friggin' door open?' she screamed. Turning round, she sprinted down the hall and outside in pursuit of the naked twins.

The young musician didn't bat an eyelid. 'I like this one,' she said. 'It was on *Songs of Praise*.' She began to play *The Old Rugged Cross*. I didn't see her father

appear in the doorway, but I did see the boot he threw at his daughter. It smashed the recorder she was holding into three pieces.

'I've told you before about playin' that fuckin' thing!' He staggered back into the living room to nurse his bruises. The little maestro picked up what was left of her instrument and ran upstairs in tears. I wanted to say something, do something, but I was only the Lecky Man. It was none of my business.

Feeling very angry, I made my way down the hall. The woman was coming back up the path with a twin under each arm. Her right hand was beginning to swell badly.

'I don't suppose I've got a divvy, 'ave I?' she asked. She was right about that (unless she was referring to her husband). I tried to talk about her daughter's talent but she wasn't interested. She walked straight past me and roared up the stairs, 'Tracy! Get down 'ere now and mind the twins!' She walked back into the living room and slammed the door behind her.

Tracy came down the stairs, still crying. Reluctantly, I made my way outside. The five-year-old was hiding in the rusting Escort and ducked down when she saw me.

The episode played on my mind for days afterwards. I talked about it so much in the office that the lads got fed up with me. Tommy always told us not to get involved

19

in the things we saw in customers' houses. 'You can't do right for wrong,' he would say, 'so leave well alone.'

On this occasion I very much wanted to ignore his advice. He told me to let it rest. 'It's happened to all of us at some time or another. You've got to forget about it.' I knew he was right but that didn't make it any easier.

Next time we visited that part of Tower Hill Estate, Tommy had arranged for Mogsy to call at A29. However, I badgered him non-stop until he agreed to swap rounds.

As I approached the house I could see the old Escort still gathering rust in the garden but, to my intense disappointment, all the windows were boarded up. The house was empty. I knocked next door and asked the woman there if she knew where they had gone.

'Somewhere in Cheshire, I heard.' They owed all kinds of money. Everyone's looking for them.' She didn't sound as if she was going to miss them very much.

I've often wondered what the world would have lost if Mozart's dad had chucked a boot at his young son, or if Beethoven's mum had slammed the piano lid down on his fingers. Even now I still sometimes think of a little girl in Kirkby and wonder what she might have made of her life if she'd been given half a chance.

THE TELEGRAM, THE CAT AND THE TORPEDO

The therapeutic value of animals has become widely recognised. Many old people's homes now actively encourage residents to bring their pets with them, knowing how valuable such companionship may be. I can well understand it. Most old people I met were devoted to their animals and a friendly pat or a few words of admiration were time-honoured guarantees of a hot cuppa on a freezing cold day. Sadly, I also witnessed their heartbreak when a beloved pet died or went missing.

One sharp November morning I was working in a road of semis in Fazakerley. Close by was a railway line that served the nearby industrial estate and Hartley's Village, a cluster of houses built by the owner of the local jam factory.

As I walked up the path on my first call, an old lady met me at the front door. She was wearing a long black coat, unbuttoned, over a pink night-dress and seemed very agitated.

'Hello, love.' I checked her name on the record card. 'Mrs Prescott, isn't it? I've come to empty your meter.'

'Oh God, I'm out of me mind with worry, lad. You haven't seen a ginger cat have you?' She was close to tears.

'Sorry, I've just started in the road.' I wished I could have been more helpful.

'He shot out the back door and he's been gone for days.' Her lips had gone blue and she was shivering with cold. She looked on the verge of collapse.

I ushered her gently back inside and did my best to reassure her. 'Don't worry! I'm sure he'll turn up. I'm in the area all day. I'll keep an eye out for him.'

'Thanks, lad. I'll put the kettle on and make a cup of tea.'

I followed her into the kitchen. The meter was above the back door which was wide open. *

'You'll need the step-ladder,' Mrs Prescott said and went to fetch it from the shed outside.

'Thanks.' I closed the door and began to climb up.

'No, don't!' Her piercing scream nearly made me fall off the ladder. She pushed past me and opened the door again. 'I want to leave it open in case he comes back.'

I didn't think this was a good idea but it was her house so I didn't argue. I unlocked the cash box and carried the money through to the living room. On the mantelpiece was a large black and white picture of a cat. Mrs Prescott brought in the tea and began to pour with an unsteady hand. I thought she was probably worrying unduly but her distress was no less real for that. Trying to cheer her up, I

---

* Some meters were put in very inconvenient places. One woman fell off a chair while putting money in her meter and tried to sue Manweb. She lost the case but afterwards Manweb spent several thousand pounds relocating awkwardly sited meters.

gestured towards the photograph.

'He certainly looks a handsome cat. What's his name?'

'We called him Guy... after Guy Fawkes.'

'Oh, right.' I remembered what I'd read about his namesake's gruesome fate and thought it better to say nothing.

'Yes, we got him on Bonfire Night. My Fred brought him home.' She looked fondly at a faded picture of a dark young man hanging on the chimney-breast. 'He's away at the moment. He'll be really upset when he finds out about Guy.' She dabbed away a tear with her hanky.

'Is there anywhere Guy might go? Could he be in a neighbour's house, do you think?'

'He could be, I suppose, though we do get a lot of rats from the jam factory. He might have chased one over there or he might be up on the railway. He might even have found himself a girlfriend.' She smiled and some of the colour began to return to her face.

I finished my tea and replaced the cash box on the meter. 'Don't worry, Mrs Prescott, I'll ask around for him. And if I see him, I'll come straight back and tell you. That's a promise. Now you keep yourself warm, do you hear?' As I said this I knew it would be difficult with the back door left open.

Working in an established area, you could usually tell who was new to the road and who had lived there for years. Many old people used to rent their houses and, as most landlords spent as little as possible on maintaining these properties, they often fell into disrepair. So double glazing, new front doors, gleaming paintwork, even the much derided stone cladding were often reliable indicators as to who the newcomers were. The next five houses I visited were all beautifully maintained. Nobody had seen a ginger cat but all agreed to check gardens and sheds on the off chance. None of them knew Mrs Prescott at all.

The sixth house had old, rotting window frames. Better still, it had a ginger cat on its front doorstep. Keeping my movements slow and my voice gentle, I inched towards him.

'Here boy... good boy... you're a handsome fellow, aren't you? Come on, boy.' At first the cat seemed very docile and I thought he was going to come to me. I moved a bit closer. 'There's a good boy. Come on, Guy.'

Suddenly Guy arched his back and spat at me. I lunged forward and tried to grab him, but he leaped onto the garden wall and ran out into the street. I shot back into the road to try and head him off but I was too late. I saw him take refuge beneath a parked car. As I knelt down to locate him, Guy then ran behind me and back up the path. This was repeated three or four more times with similar lack of success. Finally the cat ran off up the road.

I had no intention of giving up. I remembered how upset Mrs Prescott had been and was determined not to let her down. I decided to alter my strategy.

I wanted Guy to think I was no longer interested in him so, with deliberate ostentation, I crossed to the other side of the road. Out of the corner of my eye I saw him slink back to the doorstep where I'd first seen him.

I walked fifty yards, then re-crossed the road and tracked back using parked cars as cover. My superior cunning was about to win the day. Guy, happily oblivious to my tactics, had his back turned and was licking his paws unconcernedly.

I reached the last parked car and still Guy had not seen me. Now was my chance. The cat himself could not have done it better. I slipped through the open gate, padded softly up the garden path... and pounced.

It was an unequal struggle. Guy hissed and scratched as we rolled round on the ground, but to no avail. I clung on tight. He was not going to escape. My mission was accomplished.

Suddenly the front door opened. An old lady stood there, peering icily down her nose. 'And what do you think you're doing lying on my doorstep, young man?'

My face was flushed with exertion and embarrassment. 'Oh... er... it's alright . . I can explain... er... I was just... er... um... catching Mrs Prescott's cat,' I spluttered, scrambling to my feet. As I did so, Guy wriggled out of my grasp and bolted into the house.

'I see.' Her tone was neutral. She continued to look at me steadily. I felt very uncomfortable. A bead of sweat was trickling down my nose and I couldn't hold her gaze.

I found myself talking very quickly. 'Yes, I've just been up at Mrs Prescott's. Her cat's been missing for days apparently. She's very upset. I promised to keep an eye out and let her know if I saw him. Guy, his name is. I should just nip back and let her know that he's safe.' I began to retreat slowly down the path.

The expression on the old lady's face did not change. 'I shouldn't bother if I were you. The cat you've just assaulted is called Tiger and he's mine.'

I swallowed heavily and continued to back away.

'Don't you want to come in, then?' she asked. 'I assume you have come to empty my meter.'

'Er... yes... I... er... alright, then.' I didn't want to go in at all. I wanted fervently to be as far away as possible but she was on my list. Reluctantly I retraced my steps. She stepped aside to let me in, never once taking her eyes off me.

I checked her name on my record card and took a deep breath. 'Thanks, Mrs Owen.' I paused. 'Look, I'm really sorry about your cat. I feel very stupid now, but it did seem to match the description.'

Her face instantly softened. 'Don't worry, son. It wasn't really your fault. Now you go through to the back and I'll pour you a little drink. I think you need one after that.'

Five minutes later I was in her living room, sipping a delightfully large Scotch. Mrs Owen was so understanding that I felt totally relaxed. Tiger, eyeing me malevolently from a distance, was less forgiving.

'I suppose I'll have to keep looking,' I said. 'Mrs Prescott seems really fond of her cat. Her Fred brought it home on Bonfire Night, she said. That's why she called it Guy.' In the corner Tiger hissed and the hackles rose on his back.

Mrs Owen looked at him sympathetically. 'Poor old Tiger. He gets very upset when he hears that name. Can't blame the poor fellow really. Not after what he's had to put up with.'

Grateful for the sympathy, the cat walked over and jumped up onto her lap. He still regarded me with the deepest suspicion. I suppose I could hardly blame him in the circumstances.

'Does this happen often then?' I asked

'I'm afraid it does. Last month a taxi driver hurt his hand quite badly trying to catch him. Then the new vicar got stuck climbing a tree after him. The pools man was the worst. Broke his ankle chasing Tiger over a fence. They all thought he was Guy.' She mouthed the name silently. 'None of them did as well as you, though. You're the only one to actually catch him.'

I didn't know whether to feel proud of this or not.

'Went off his food after the incident with the double glazing salesman,' she said, fondling Tiger's head. 'Vet said he was suffering from stress so I kept him in for a fortnight. Today's the first day he's been out again. That's why I was a little bit annoyed.'

As she spoke, I was becoming vaguely aware something didn't sound right. 'Hang on a minute! How many times has Guy gone missing then?'

Tiger jumped down and walked through into the kitchen. He'd clearly heard enough of that name for one day.

'I think I'd better explain. It all started when Mrs Prescott's husband was killed by a torpedo in the Second World War.'

'What ship was he on?' I asked automatically. My dad had fought in the Battle of the Atlantic – as he never tired of telling us – and I reckoned that I knew every detail of it.

'He wasn't on a ship.' Mrs Owen gave a wry smile. 'He was a supervisor in a munitions factory in Birmingham. Apparently, a torpedo rolled off a shelf on top of him. Killed him outright. It was so sad.'

I thought of the young man in the photograph. 'So who's Fred then? Is he her second husband?'

'No, it was Fred who was killed by the torpedo.'

I was becoming more and more confused. I was sure Mrs Prescott had spoken of him in the present tense. 'I don't understand. How could he have brought a cat home if he was dead?'

'He brought it home in 1941. It went missing the following year during the May Blitz. There was an ammunition train nearby that took a direct hit. Blew out all the windows in the road. Mrs Prescott was claustrophobic so she wouldn't go into the Anderson shelter. She sat in the kitchen with the cat on her knee and the back door open. When the train blew up, the cat shot out of the door never to be seen again. Happened only a month after Fred died, too. Guy was one of the last presents Fred gave her. I suppose that's why she's still trying to find him.'

'Poor woman!' I remembered Mrs Prescott's scream of anguish when I closed the kitchen door. 'So she's left her back door open ever since?'

'No.' Mrs Owen looked at me pityingly. 'She's got worse in the last couple of years, but she's not always this bad. She's forgotten to take her medication. I'll go up and see her in a minute.'

She didn't have to. As I was leaving, Mrs Prescott was standing by Mrs Owen's gate. In her hand was an old, dog-eared telegram. She looked at my uniform.

'Are you the young man from the Post Office? I think you delivered this to the wrong house.'

I didn't know what to do so I took the telegram and read it. It was dated 15 April 1942.

'WE REGRET TO INFORM YOU THAT FREDERICK PRESCOTT HAS BEEN KILLED AS THE RESULT OF AN ACCIDENT.'

That was all it said. No details, no thanks for services rendered. It could not have been more terse.

Mrs Prescott looked at me appealingly. 'It's alright, you know. Fred's coming home this weekend.'

I was born in 1950 and grew up with all sorts of stories about the Second World War but never before had any touched me so closely. I stood with a lump in my throat as Mrs Owen slipped past and took her friend by the arm.

'Come on, Stella, I'll walk you back home. You haven't taken your tablets this morning, have you? You know you have to take them every day.'

As I turned to shut the gate, I looked back at Tiger standing in the doorway. He was sniffing the air and looking about him nervously. Was there lurking another mad, motiveless assailant, ready to pounce without warning? Poor old Tiger! Even though he wasn't born till nearly forty years after it ended, he too was a casualty of the Second World War.

Miracle on Upper Parly Street

Liverpool's Chinatown, situated in the shadow of the city's Anglican Cathedral, is the oldest known Chinese community in Western Europe. Until recently their unique culture was largely ignored by the 'natives', but happily the Chinese New Year is now celebrated by thousands of ordinary Liverpudlians.

My great affection for the Chinese was reinforced one day under the most trying circumstances. Upper Parliament Street is close to the southern boundary of Chinatown, and number twenty-eight, like many properties in and around Toxteth, was a large house converted into flats. Mr Kim San Wah lived on the ground floor, but none of the collectors liked calling at his house because of the chickens he kept in his front room. He had at least twenty, but every time the Environmental Health inspector came to follow up complaints, the chickens would vanish into thin air.

'Dead clever those Chinese, you know!' Tommy said, 'volunteering' me to empty Mr Wah's meter. 'Rule the world one day they will.' He had fought in the Far East, so who could argue with him? I left the office to a barrage of farmyard noises. The lads were all enjoying themselves at my expense.

I pulled up outside Mr Wah's flat. Even with the van windows closed I could hear the sound of reggae music. As I stepped onto the pavement I realised that a live band was playing somewhere inside the house.

I hammered on the front door for a couple of minutes, then banged on Mr Wah's window. The curtain moved and an old Chinese face appeared. I mouthed the word 'Manweb' at him and held up my case. Above the music I could just make out Mr Wah's reply.

'All chickens gone. Tell man all gone!' he insisted, shaking his head vehemently. As he dropped the curtain a large cockerel jumped up onto the window ledge and pecked at the glass. I banged again, this time holding up a bag of coins. He lifted the curtain and his eyes lit up when he realised who I was. The cockerel was less enthusiastic, eyeing me with suspicion as if I was a threat to his hens.

Mr Wah opened the door and had to shout over the din from upstairs where the drummer was endeavouring to come through the ceiling and join us.

'Come in, come in. Velly good see you. This way please.' Mr Wah bent down just in time to stop one of his chickens escaping. As soon as I stepped inside, the smell hit me in the stomach. I turned and took a final breath of fresh air to stave off the nausea.

'No! You stay please! Empty meter!' As Mr Wah grabbed my elbow, the chicken he was holding made another attempt to escape. It got as far as my head where it perched for a few seconds before jumping back into Mr Wah's arms. Meanwhile, six more chickens had ambled out into the hall. Mr Wah booted them back in with a skill which a sober Georgie Best could not have bettered.

As I went to enter Mr Wah's flat, I noticed a goat at the top of the stairs, tied to the banister by a rope. The goat was happily chewing the rope and seemed unaffected by the rock concert. Not so Mr Wah. He pushed past me and stood at the bottom of the stairs.

'Stop music... frighten chickens... bastards!' He then launched into a torrent of Chinese interspersed with a few more *bastards*.

The rock concert stopped abruptly. All was quiet except for Mr Wah's voice and his agitated chickens. Then a naked West Indian, with dreadlocks and a Fender bass slung over his shoulder, appeared at the top of the stairs.

'What de problem, man? You gonna upset de goat.' He patted the animal's head, seemingly unconcerned that its mouth was within nibbling distance of his own irritatingly impressive manhood. 'I'm gonna make some spicy sauce and come down and barbecue dem chickens.' He took the bass guitar off his shoulder and played some chords.

'Bastard! You leave chickens 'lone. I tell policeman 'bout you if you touch chickens!' He let loose another volley of Chinese, only this time without any *bastards*. Presumably he had remembered some oriental swear words. The bass player turned round and went back to his room.

The band played even louder as I followed Mr Wah into his front room, where I was greeted by an incongruous sight. The floor was filthy with chicken droppings, but in the middle of the room stood a magnificent eight-seater banquet table that would have graced any boardroom or hotel. Resting grandly on it was a gleaming silver punch bowl with silver cups hanging round the edge. Amazingly, the tabletop was free of any droppings.

The rest of the room was a farmyard. Running along one wall was a plastic gutter mounted at intervals on bricks. Mr Wah picked up a bag of seed and poured it along the gutter. The chickens came running and began to feed excitedly.

Mr Wah opened the meter cupboard and picked up three eggs from a little bed of straw. 'I make you omelette. Velly nice.'

I hadn't eaten for hours but the smell inside the room had rather dulled my appetite. I declined his offer politely.

As I removed the box from the meter, Mr Wah took a cloth from his pocket, polished the table, then put down a newspaper for me to count on. Peace descended. The reggae band took a break, the chickens went quiet after feeding and Mr Wah sat back contentedly in his chair.

I allowed my curiosity to get the better of me. 'It's a very beautiful table. Where did you get it?'

'My friend, Mr Copper ask me to mind table for him before he go on holiday. Funny man, Mr Copper! He watch lot of television. He ask me to mind them while he away.' Mr Wah smiled every time I tipped more money out of the box. 'Ten television Mr Copper got. All in cellar with whisky. Mr Copper drink lot of whisky. Fifty cases he got. I mind them till he come back from holiday.'

While he was talking, a chicken jumped onto his lap and Mr Wah stroked it as he would a cat. The rest of the chickens had settled under the table and looked ready to sleep.

'Where has Mr Copper gone for his holiday?' I asked. Mr Copper sounded an interesting person, to say the least.

'I think he gone on ship called HMP Kirkham. Must be velly nice. He been gone three months. He said for me to keep eye on things and he would polish them off when he get back. But table get lot of dust on it in cellar, so I get my cousin and we bring it up and polish it for him.'

I was just about to tell him that Kirkham was a prison, not a ship, when the band decided to wake up the world. The whole house shook. The chickens, startled, tried to take flight but crashed into the table. The shock wave knocked over the money I was counting.

'Bastard!' Almost by magic a meat cleaver appeared in Mr Wah's hand. Clearly he had reached the end of his tether. He rushed through the door closely followed by a stampede of chickens.

Meanwhile, the goat had not only come to the end of its tether but slipped it altogether. It came charging down the stairs at the abusive Chinaman and his chickens. Still seated at the table, I had a grandstand view. Mr Wah and his chickens arrived at the foot of the stairs just in time for the goat to land on top of them. Struggling to keep its feet on the tiles in the hall, the goat lowered its head ominously at Mr Wah. The meat cleaver may as well have been a feather duster for all the good it was to him. He made no attempt to use it. He ran back into the room pursued by the chickens and the goat.

'Bastard... bastard goat... go away!' They did three laps of the table before they stopped, with Mr Wah at one end and the goat at the other. I managed to bag all the coins before they could fall over again. Mr Wah shimmied left, then right, to try and confuse his assailant but the goat was not to be denied. It charged right under the table.

My neutrality was threatened as the goat crashed into my legs. I winced at the impact and just managed to climb onto the chair before it could attack me again. Undeterred, the goat retreated momentarily, then put its head down and with great force slammed itself into the leg of the table. All the cups fell off the punch bowl.

'Bastard... shit... Mr Copper!' Suddenly everything went still. What had happened to the goat? Was this a deliberate ploy to catch us off our guard? Apprehensively, we looked under the table.

The goat lay motionless on the floor while the chickens gathered round like ghoulish bystanders at a road accident.

Mr Wah began to shake. 'What I do now? Bastard upstairs roast chickens.' He looked at me in appeal.

'Drag it out into the hall! They might think it fell down the stairs.'

Mr Wah didn't look too hopeful but did as I suggested, dragging the body over to the bottom of the stairs. Perspiration glistened on his forehead. The reggae band was still playing but something was different.

'What de fuck going on man?' I now realised what it was. There was no bass.

'Goat fall down stairs... I try wake him up... old Chinese remedy,' said Mr Wah nervously.

The bass player did not look happy. He walked downstairs, still naked, guitar slung over his shoulder. I prayed that, like many musicians of the time, he was heavily into peace and love. He bent down and picked up the goat's lifeless body. 'Hendrix! Come on, man, wake up! Don't die on me, man!'

The rest of the band stopped playing. One by one they filed out onto the landing, some naked, others half-dressed in shorts or jeans. 'What's up, Leroy?' one of them asked. 'Everything OK, man?' Leroy shook his head sadly and carried the goat upstairs.

Suddenly the goat began to twitch. Leroy's expression was transformed. 'Look!

It's opened its eyes!... It's a miracle. It's a happening, man! We gotta do a song about this.' By the time he'd reached the top of the stairs, the goat was trying to wriggle out of his arms.

Mr Wah, myself and the chickens stood in silence at the bottom. Leroy, smiling, tied the goat to the banister, then turned and ran back down. 'Thanks, man, you saved his life.' He embraced Mr Wah, almost lifting him off the floor. Anxious to avoid a similar expression of gratitude, I slipped unobtrusively back into the flat followed by the chickens.

Mr Wah came back in and closed the door. 'He no roast chickens now. Chickens safe.' He did a little jig of joy around the room.

To complete his good fortune I gave him his divvy of £15. In return he presented me with six eggs, then slapped me so hard on the back that I nearly dropped them. Beaming broadly, he led me back into the hall where we bowed to each other and said goodbye. Once outside, I sucked in two large lungfuls of fresh air and wondered if anyone would ever believe what had happened.

'Excuse me, do you live in these flats?' Two men in grey suits stood in front of me. One had a clipboard with the words *Environmental Health* on it.

'No, I've just been working in there.'

They looked disappointed. 'You don't know the landlord by any chance, do you? Mr Cooper, his name is.' I was tempted to say that he'd gone on an extended cruise but I didn't.

I sat in the van and watched them bang on Mr Wah's window. Strains of the band's new song, *Goat Resurrection*, drowned out their attempts to gain access. Finally, Mr Wah opened the door and let them in. I had to stay. I wanted to see their faces when they came out.

Their visit was obviously far less eventful than mine. They were out within five minutes. 'How does he do it?' one of them said as they walked past. 'Where does he hide them?'

His companion shook his head, mystified. 'I don't know. Dead clever these Chinese. Rule the world one day, they will.' It could have been Tommy speaking.

I started up the engine and began to drive away. As I passed his window, Mr Wah lifted the curtain and waved at me while a chicken pecked happily away at the windowpane.

JUST A GIGOLO

The Liverpool Empire in Lime Street has seen many fine performances over the years. I was fortunate to witness one, which was truly dramatic in the way it plucked triumph from the jaws of disaster. However, for me, the story did not have such a happy ending.

PROLOGUE

It all started quite promisingly. As I entered the office one afternoon, Tommy called me over. 'Some woman rang for you. She said could you call her back, it's important.'

I didn't recognise the number and was very curious so I called straight away. The phone was answered by a very refined voice.

'Is that my Electric Man? This is Nora Smyth here. I'm sorry to bother you.' She sounded a little nervous. 'I don't know if you remember – Larkhill Lane, Clubmoor. You emptied my meter last Tuesday.' I certainly did remember. We'd spent thirty-five minutes discussing our mutual love of classical music and opera. She had an extensive collection of records which I'd spent a long time admiring. 'Look, I hope you don't think I'm being too forward but I've got two tickets to see *Tosca* at the Empire on Friday. I was wondering if you'd like to come with me.'

'I'd love to but I'll have to check first,' I replied. 'Can I ring you back?' I wasn't sure what company policy was about fraternising with customers. Did meter readers have their own version of the Hippocratic oath? There was only one way to find out so I asked Tommy.

He was characteristically blunt. 'It's alright as long as you don't get her pregnant.'

I knew that the prospect was remote. I was as red-blooded as the next fellow but the forty year age gap did make a difference. Foolishly, I mentioned this to Tommy and soon it was all round the office. The other lads thought Christmas had come early.

'Which club are you going on to afterwards?' asked Mogsy. 'Darby and Joan or British Legion?'

'Will you be dining out,' said Big Ron, 'or are Meals on Wheels coming round?'

Ace was next. 'There's a good pub near the theatre, Dave. I believe they do a very nice mug of Horlicks.'

'Do you want my granny for Christmas dinner?' offered Armpit, but I was ready for this one.

'No thanks, I'd prefer to stick with the turkey!'

Come Friday evening, I called for Nora in a taxi. She had dressed for the occasion and looked most ladylike in a suede hat and long red coat fastened with gold buttons. She must have been a real heartbreaker in her youth. Even now she appeared animated and alert. Her eyes were sparkling and I guessed she was really looking forward to the evening.

'Mustn't forget this.' Nora picked up an elegant black leather handbag from the hall table. 'It's got my medicine in it. I have to take it every night.' She opened the bag to check she hadn't forgotten anything. 'Right, I'm ready.'

I followed her down the garden path to the waiting taxi. Graciously, she stepped aside and allowed me to open the door for her. 'Thank you, young man,' she said politely. It could have been a duchess speaking.

When we arrived at the Empire I went to pay off the taxi, but Nora put a restraining hand on my arm. 'No, no, I invited you.' She slipped three five-pound notes into my hand. 'You settle up with the driver. The rest will pay for our refreshments.'

We were half an hour early so we went to the bar upstairs for a drink. Over a large Scotch Nora told me something about herself. She'd been a widow for five years and had two sons and a daughter, all now living down south. When she was younger she'd done a bit of amateur dramatics which, she said, gave her a natural affinity with performers. Her husband had never shared her enthusiasm for opera – 'a lot of people making a lot of noise' – but used to go with her from a sense of duty.

'He was a man of very simple tastes, God bless him, but he did have a good heart.' Nora smiled fondly at his memory.

'I hope you didn't mind my inviting you this evening,' she went on, 'but I don't really like going to the theatre on my own. And you seemed so knowledgeable when you came to my house. It'll be nice having an escort who understands what's going on.'

'I bet you say that to all the men,' I replied.

Nora laughed. 'No, I mean it. Thank you for coming with me.'

By now it was getting closer to seven thirty so I suggested we should take our seats. Nora, though, was in no hurry to move. 'I prefer to leave it late. That way, you don't have to keep standing up for other people. Let's have another drink.'

We got into the auditorium with a minute to spare. I put Nora's seat down for her and helped her off with her coat. As we settled ourselves, Nora waved to a couple of elderly woman in the row behind.

'Two spinster ladies from the Wirral,' she explained. 'Retired music teachers. We come across each other occasionally when the opera comes to town.'

In fact, the opera didn't come to town very often. And when it did – like tonight – interest was moderate. Though this was a one-night only performance – admittedly by a little-known company – the theatre was only half full. The good people of Liverpool didn't know what they were missing.

I've never known why opera is considered such a highbrow form of entertainment. Take *Tosca*, for example. What more could you want? It's got everything: love, lust, jealousy, deception, betrayal, violent death – and big tits! Not much different from your average soap really. I can't understand why it's not more popular – unless it's because everything's in Italian.

An expectant hush descended on the auditorium as the loudspeaker crackled into life.

'Ladies and gentlemen, *Opera di Brescia* regrets to announce that the baritone, Francesco Grappasoni, is indisposed. The role of Baron Scarpia will tonight be sung by Roberto Falitoso. We do hope you will enjoy the performance.'

There were one or two murmurs of disappointment. Then the lights dimmed and the curtain went up on early nineteenth century Rome.

ACT ONE

The trembling, dishevelled figure of Angelotti, an escaped political prisoner, creeps furtively into the church of Sant' Andrea della Valle. He conceals himself in a vault and waits for dusk. The painter, Mario Cavaradossi, arrives to finish working on a portrait. He is recognised by the desperate Angelotti who approaches him for help. Enter the magnificent cleavage of the virtuous heroine, Tosca, followed shortly by the lady herself.

Deeply jealous, Tosca wrongly suspects Cavaradossi of two-timing her and throws a wobbler (literally). He reassures her of his love and she goes away, satisfied. Nora opens her handbag and takes a sip from her medicine bottle.

Cavaradossi resumes his conversation with Angelotti. With typical male generosity, he offers to hide the fugitive at his villa, where there is a secret chamber in a well. A cannon sounds. Angelotti's escape has been discovered (Group 4 weren't around then, were they?) and the two men take their leave.

The church slowly fills with people and a hymn of thanksgiving is sung to celebrate a supposed victory over Napoleon. However, the mood of rejoicing is suddenly cut short. The atmosphere becomes thick with menace as the evil Chief of Police, Baron Scarpia, enters. With incisive questioning he begins to piece together what has happened. Nora takes some more medicine, then offers some to me. I refuse. Why should I want any medicine? I'm feeling perfectly well.

When Tosca returns, Scarpia spins his Iago-like web and plays upon her jealousy. Cunningly, he orders his henchmen to follow her, knowing she will lead him straight to Angelotti. His fiendishly wicked plot begins to unfold.

This, at least, was how Puccini saw it. Unfortunately we didn't. Poor Signor Falitoso conveyed less a sense of menace than of pathos. He was a slight, totally inoffensive sort of man, so small that his face was on a level with Tosca's cleavage. Sadly, he had no chance to enjoy the view, as his wig seemed to slip down over his eyes every time he moved. As if this wasn't bad enough, his costume was three sizes too big for him as well. Nora said he reminded her of Norman Wisdom. After that I kept waiting for Mr Grimsdale to appear.

Unlike traditional theatre, opera performers sometimes take a bow after each act. Tosca and Cavaradossi received the loudest applause. There was a polite ripple for Scarpia.

INTERVAL

Nora's exit was a complete reversal of her entrance – last in, first out – so I didn't have to wait long at the bar. When I came back with the drinks, Nora had been joined by the two Wirral spinsters. Both looked very prim and respectable, like floor walkers at George Henry Lee. They were obviously intrigued by my presence, looking up quizically as I sat down, but Nora made no attempt to introduce us.

Curiosity finally got the better of one. 'Is this your son, then?' she asked.

Nora laughed in surprise. 'Good gracious, no! He's far too young to be my son. He's my date.' Their jaws dropped in unison. 'This one's got a bit of culture for a change,' she went on, warming to her theme. 'After all,' – she gave me a sly little wink – 'I've not picked him for his looks, have I?'

The spinsters' faces settled into identical expressions halfway between disbelief and disgust. And despite some further prompting – 'Will you and your... er... friend be going to see *Rigoletto* in Llandudno next week?' – Nora would not be drawn further on the subject. We had one more drink and then returned to the auditorium. I noticed there were now some more empty seats.

ACT TWO

We are now in Scarpia's apartment at the palace. His villainous plan has not entirely succeeded. Angelotti's still at large, but at least Cavaradossi's helping them with their enquiries. He is taken out and brutally tortured but will not reveal his friend's whereabouts. (What a hero!) Nora takes a large swig of medicine. Her face is flushed and her eyes look a bit glazed.

Meanwhile Tosca has been summoned by Scarpia. Her cleavage trembles alarmingly as she hears her lover's anguished cries. Tormented by his desperate plight, she reveals the fugitive's hiding place. Cavaradossi curses her angrily. But Scarpia's men are too late. Angelotti has committed suicide and cheated the gallows. Still, not to worry. They can always take it out on Cavaradossi. There's nothing down for him at all.

Tosca, distraught, implores Scarpia to spare her lover's life. Scarpia says there is a way out, but it'll cost her. Tosca's interested if the price is right. It's not. Scarpia pushes his wig higher up his head and reveals his shameful proposition: get your knickers off and lover boy goes free. Tosca sinks to her knees in despair. So much for a lifetime of piety and good works!

35

Scarpia takes a more practical view. *'A me una vita, a te chieggo un'istante'* – 'You ask a life of me, I of you a quickie on the sofa.' (Fair point, I've always thought!)

Tosca is forced to agree to Scarpia's foul offer. Scarpia's wig is now so insecure, he seems to have one hand almost permanently on his head. He tells her Cavaradossi won't be hanged, but put before a firing squad instead. (That's a great comfort, isn't it!) 'Ah, but don't worry, they'll be using blanks.' Tosca is taken in by this cruel deception while Nora finishes off the last of her medicine. I feel a bit foolish as I finally realise it's whisky.

Tension mounts as the villain moves forward to embrace Tosca in a frenzy of sexual excitement, then evaporates as he is seized by a bout of coughing. To clear his throat he picks up and drinks the glass of wine he's just poured out for Tosca. God knows what it really is but most of it ends up spluttered over Tosca's cleavage. She almost hits a top 'C' as she tries to compose herself.

As the act moves to its inexorable and bloody climax, Scarpia's performance becomes more and more Wisdomesque. The lust motif sounds as Scarpia tries his luck again. His other hand is now holding up his trousers. (Why bother in the

36

circumstances?) Tosca, unkindly, makes no allowances for his problem. She's still playing hard to get.

'*Non ancora*' – 'Not yet.' She asks Scarpia for a note giving her and her lover safe passage out of Rome. Scarpia agrees, takes a pen from his desk, drops it and crawls under the desk to retrieve it. As he gets up he bangs his head, knocking his wig violently askew. Finally he signs on the dotted line and advances on Tosca to claim his long-awaited prize. You did have some sympathy for the fellow. After all he'd been through you had to admit he deserved it.

In a final paroxysm of lust, he reaches for her. '*Tosca, finalmente mia!*' – 'Tosca, you are finally mine!' But he hasn't reckoned with the innate treachery of womankind. Tosca flourishes a knife she's just nicked from Scarpia's table and plunges it deep into his cold, black heart.

'*Questo e il bacio de Tosca!*' – 'This is the kiss of Tosca!' – she cries in triumph as horns and woodwind hammer out the theme of deception. '*Muori dannato! Muori!*' – 'Die, you fiend! Die!'

Poor Scarpia realises he's been betrayed, and his exclamation of joy turns into a terrible and despairing cry.

'*Maledetta! Aiuto Muoro!*' – God damn you! Help...Mr Grimsdale!'

In a gesture of forgiveness, the faithless Tosca places two candles by Scarpia's head (so typical of a woman – too little too late) and leaves. The lights dim and the villain's body lies motionless, visible only by candlelight. The wig, dislodged by his fall, lies equally motionless alongside. Finally the curtain falls on surely the worst performance of Scarpia ever seen.

ACT TWO AND A HALF

As the cast took their curtain call, applause was muted, rising briefly when Tosca stepped forward. As was traditional, Scarpia was left alone to take the final bow. There was some sympathetic and embarrassed applause, which quickly died out. Scarpia's shoulders sagged as he turned and began to troop off dejectedly.

Nora leant across to whisper in my ear. Her words were a little slurred and the refined accent had vanished, but compassion for a fellow thespian shone through. 'Ah, God love him, he did his best. He's some poor mother's son.' Suddenly she leapt to her feet with a sprightliness that belied her years and shouted at the top of her voice, 'Bravo!' She clapped enthusiastically, then put two fingers in her mouth and whistled like a docker summoning a taxi. 'Bravo!' she called again. 'Bravo!'

Scarpia stopped suddenly in his tracks and peered out into the auditorium. Was this one final twist of the knife, fate tormenting him with the most merciless sarcasm? Nora carried on clapping. 'Bravo!'

Her response was infectious. I found myself joining in and others quickly followed suit. Soon, all those who remained in the theatre were standing, their applause and cries of appreciation thundering all round the building.

The effect on Scarpia was galvanising. He stood stock-still, chest proudly thrust forward, back ramrod stiff, eyes welling up with tears. Then, to the greatest roar I have ever heard in a theatre, he removed his wig (this time it was deliberate) and, flourishing it like a hat, bowed flamboyantly.

The applause showed no sign of diminishing. Scarpia walked forward and pointed at Nora before placing both hands over his heart and blowing her a kiss. Now totally overwhelmed, he sank to his knees and began to sob openly. Blowing kisses to everyone, he staggered to his feet, holding tightly onto the curtain for support.

Hysteria seemed to grip the whole audience. The more Scarpia acknowledged the applause, the louder it became. People couldn't stop cheering, whistling and clapping. Even the orchestra, caught up in the glorious madness of it all, were giving him a standing ovation.

Scarpia was a man possessed. Like a little India-rubber man, he kept bowing elaborately in all directions, head almost touching the floor. Backstage, they must have been wondering how they'd ever get him off.

Eventually Tosca came out carrying a huge bouquet which she presented to the new star. Tears coursed down his cheeks as she kissed him and hugged him tightly to her bosom. He disappeared momentarily and I was afraid he was going to suffocate. The audience were still cheering and whistling as she took him by the hand and led him firmly off the stage, but not before he had given one final triumphant wave to his adoring public.

Exhausted, we sank back into our seats. Even the Wirral spinsters had been overcome, probably for the first time in their lives.

ACT THREE

Whatever followed was bound to be anti-climax. Nora's out of whisky and Tosca thinks she's got away with it. 'It's all been sorted. Play dead and when they've gone, we'll do a runner.' When she finds out the bullets are real and her boyfriend's a goner, she throws herself off the battlements. End of story.

Applause was moderate at the final curtain call. No-one had much emotion left. Scarpia didn't reappear. He'd obviously decided not to push his luck too far.

Nora sounded quite disappointed. 'I wonder what's happened to Scarpia.'

I thought for a moment. Not just picked for his looks, eh! I felt I owed Nora one. 'Haven't you heard?' I said. 'He's been rushed off to hospital. Heart trouble.'

Nora gasped and looked shocked. 'Oh, dear God, no. I feel terrible. I started it all off.'

I did my best to reassure her. 'Don't blame yourself! It's just one of those things.'

'Oh God, the poor man! The excitement must've been too much for him. What happened exactly?'

I tried to be casual. 'Didn't you notice? He got stabbed at the end of Act Two.' Nora roared with laughter and, for the first time in my life, I was assaulted by an old age pensioner's handbag.

EPILOGUE

Outside the theatre we were queuing for a taxi. The Wirral spinsters were just in front of us, still trying to establish exactly who I was. 'Did you get him from an agency?' one of them asked, abandoning any pretence at tact.

Nora laughed and shook her head. 'Of course not. I'm not going to pay, am I? I just cruise the bars until I find a good one.'

The spinsters pursed their lips even more tightly.

The taxi took us back to Nora's. I got out and escorted her to the door.

'I won't invite you in, love. I'm feeling a bit light-headed. But thanks for a lovely evening.' She put her arms around me and gave me a big hug. 'We must do this again. I haven't enjoyed myself so much for years.'

'I'd be happy to,' I replied. And I meant it. I'd had a great time. Nora, especially the inebriated version, was a lively and entertaining companion. And, though 'Falitoso at the Empire' lacked the clout of 'Pavarotti at La Scala', I wouldn't have missed Scarpia's performance for the world.

But, alas, it was not to be. Such is the fickleness of woman. Months later Tosca's knife was plunged through my own heart. I too was betrayed. All those fine words – 'it'll be nice having an escort who understands what's going on', 'this one's got a bit of culture for a change', 'we must do this again' – all empty, all meaningless. It hurts me to think about it even now. When *La Boheme* came to Liverpool, Nora only went and invited the gasman. If I ever see the Wirral spinsters again, I'll make sure they know the whole sordid truth.

LOVE AT FIRST BITE

Love is a many splendoured thing says the song, and it's true. Love can make music, swim oceans, move mountains. It makes kings relinquish their thrones, men sacrifice their lives, even bachelors give up their freedom. One of the finest examples of love that I ever witnessed occurred on a cold January day in the early seventies.

I was working in some flats near Scotland Road. They offered splendid views over the River Mersey, but the long, open landings, especially on the upper storeys, were exposed to the bitter wind which cut through to your very bones. With outdoor meter cupboards and coins that felt like ice cubes, I longed for the end of the day and a nice warm fire.

I'd been working three hours without one offer of a cuppa. Convinced frostbite had started its second course on my fingers, I considered going off sick. My next call was going to be the last.

The door opened slowly and an old weathered face eased itself into view. It belonged to a little old lady who looked well into her eighties. She was wearing a wrap-around pinny over a faded blue dress. She peered at me closely.

'Sorry, it was all a mistake last time. We don't want communion. We're not 'catlicks', you see.'

As she started to close the door, I put out my hand. 'Hang on a minute, love. I've only come to empty your meter.'

'Sorry, son. I thought you were a priest.' She fetched me the key to the meter cupboard and turned to walk back up the hall. But not before she had uttered those wonderful, magical words, 'Would you like a nice cup of tea?'

I opened the cupboard and carried the box through into her living room. It was like stepping into an Aladdin's cave. Every inch of space on the walls and shelves seemed to be occupied by different kinds of trinkets, ornaments and souvenirs.

Grace and Stanley Spicer had been married sixty years. This was commemorated by a beautiful plaque that hung proudly beside their wedding photograph. Inscribed on the plaque were the names of their five sons with a picture of Grace and Stanley glazed into the middle. They must have been in their early twenties when the picture was taken and a very handsome couple they made too; Grace holding a bouquet of roses, Stanley standing proudly alongside. They wouldn't have been out of place on the cover of a Mills and Boon novel.

In the centre of the room stood a large table covered by a plastic tablecloth. Printed on the cloth was a huge red dragon with the words *Tai Shan Restaurant Hong Kong* beneath its feet.

'Have you been to Hong Kong then?' I asked, tipping the frozen coins onto the dragon's tail.

'No, our Jimmy gave us that,' she said proudly. Then she gave me a guided tour of the living room walls telling me the name of each son and which ornaments he had brought back. All five sons had gone away to sea and every return trip produced new trinkets from exotic, far-away places. There were a variety of dolls in national costume, bark paintings from Mexico, a set of carved wooden elephants, a bonsai plant, a silk wall-hanging from Japan, Spanish mantillas and many, many more. Grace's eyes sparkled as she spoke of her sons and their gifts.

Our conversation was suddenly interrupted when the big armchair by the fire erupted into heavy, rasping coughs. Or so I first thought. I looked more closely and saw a shrivelled old man sunk deep into the upholstery. Clothes, skin, teeth, even the soggy cigarette dangling from his lips, were of the same dingy brown as the chair. That's why I'd not immediately recognised him as a separate entity.

Grace looked over at him tenderly. 'Do you want your spray, Stan?'

He waved an arm feebly. 'No thanks, love,' he replied between coughs. The fire hissed as he leant forward and spat a huge globule of phlegm onto the coals. He sank back into the chair, indifferent to the two Zulu warriors on the wall above who were pointing their spears at his head.

Grace opened the door to the kitchen releasing a cloud of steam. I could just make out an enamel bucket bubbling merrily away on the cooker. She picked up a wooden spoon and fished out a pair of off-white underpants. She held them to the light as if checking for stains, then dropped them back into the bucket.

She returned carrying a dark wooden tray inlaid with diaphanous pink and white mother-of-pearl – 'Our Tommy bought this in Yokohama'; a teapot whose spout was shaped like an elephant's trunk – 'Our Billy got this in Bangkok'; and silver spoons marked *Waldorf Hotel*, – 'Our Albie picked these up in New York. Don't suppose they'll miss them.' The mugs were of a more local provenance. Mine had *The Glorious Twelfth* emblazoned on it. I didn't think of Scotty Road as a big grouse-shooting area and, sure enough, when I picked it up, there on the other side was King Billy, sword raised triumphantly, astride his trusty white charger. I figured the priest never got a cup of tea.

I stacked and counted the ice cubes, then thawed out my frozen fingers on the hot mug. Soon I was basking in the warmth of the coal fire and the tea inside me. An old ship's clock – 'Our Richie gave us that for our anniversary' – ticked steadily on the wall. In the kitchen the gas jets gave the occasional gentle hiss as water boiled over from the bucket. I felt my eyes growing very heavy.

I would probably have nodded off had not Stan been seized by another bout of heavy, wheezing coughs. His whole body shook as he struggled for breath. He looked awfully frail and very, very old. As Grace sprayed the medicine down his throat, I saw once more how badly stained his teeth were. It was hard to believe that here was the dashing young groom of the wedding photo.

When Stan was comfortable again, Grace brought a plateful of thick, freshly-made sandwiches in from the kitchen. It never ceased to amaze me how hospitable some people could be.

'Here you are, son. Take a few. You need to keep your strength up in this weather.'

She passed one to Stan, then took one herself and dipped it into her tea. With great dexterity she lowered her head and flicked the sodden morsel into her mouth just before it disintegrated. She saw me looking at her and proffered an explanation. 'Got no teeth.'

'Must be very awkward for you,' I commiserated.

'Got used it now. Have to soak everything before I can eat it.' As she spoke, she sprayed me with crumbs of bread and cheese.

'Haven't you got any dentures?' I braced myself for another salvo of soggy crumbs.

'Had new false teeth before Christmas. Hurt like buggery, they did. Spent more time in me pocket than me mouth' She bobbed her head to catch another morsel before it dropped off. It was reminiscent of a tortoise I'd once fed at Chester Zoo.

I tried to be helpful. 'Can't you take them back and get the dentist to change them?'

'Haven't got them any more. Fell out me pocket on the way back from bingo. Good riddance, I say.'

I thought it was time to leave before I became too settled so I rose from the table. Grace stood up and took a bowl of Brazil nuts from the sideboard.

'Help yourself, son. We got these for Christmas. Take some home with you.'

I shook my head. 'No thanks, I don't like nuts very much.'

'I love them. Quite fancy some now, actually.' She took a handful from the bowl. I looked at her, intrigued. How on earth was she going to eat them? She wouldn't have much joy dunking Brazil nuts.

I watched with interest as Grace cracked one open, then got up and walked across to Stan's chair. 'Don't mind, do you, love?'

Stan smiled gently up at her. 'You go ahead, dear.' He took out his own teeth and passed them to her as tenderly as if they were a rose.

Grace slipped them into her mouth and bit into the nut. The dentures were too big for her and rattled round her mouth like an olly in a cathedral but she seemed happy enough, jaws munching contentedly up and down. Not so myself. My stomach heaved and I felt I was going to be sick. Repulsed, I looked away, only to catch sight of Stan grinning gummily across at her.

This is obscene, I thought, the most disgusting thing I've seen in my entire life. But then I looked again at Stan and saw his eyes gleaming with pride. As the initial shock wore off, I suddenly thought, well, why not? If you truly love someone, then surely you'd be willing to share everything. And, if necessary, doesn't that also include teeth?

I eventually bid the lovebirds farewell and left. As I stepped out onto the landing, a tall figure was approaching, overcoat collar turned up against the wind. When he got closer, I saw he was a priest. Out of curiosity I turned to watch him. He stopped momentarily outside Grace's door, checked the number and quickly moved on. He wasn't going to make the same mistake twice.

Across the river, a ship was slowly pulling into dock. I found myself wondering what gifts the sailors on board were bringing home to their loved ones. But, whatever they were, I knew that nothing, not all the pearls of the orient nor the richest jewel in the world, could have ever been more precious than that dirty set of teeth.

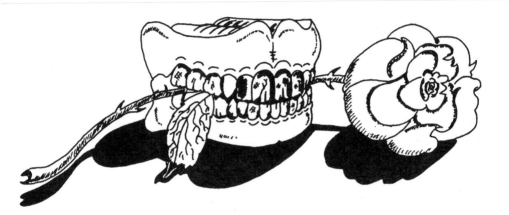

THE MERRY WIDOW

'Avoid funerals like the death!' Tommy told me when I first started. 'Never go into a house when there's a funeral on!' This was good advice – I only wish I'd followed it. One particular funeral still makes my head spin whenever I think of it.

I was working in Bedford Road in Bootle, when I saw a mountain of wreaths on a doorstep a couple of houses ahead. I checked my records and, finding it on my list, wrote down *No call because of funeral* alongside the address. This was standard procedure to satisfy the office.

As I passed the house I lowered my head respectfully. However, riotous noises from within made me cast a surreptitious sideways glance. The front door was open and people were standing in the hall laughing and drinking. They were certainly putting a brave face on their mourning.

I was ten yards past the gate when suddenly an arm was flung round my throat. My head was twisted violently to one side, forcing me face to face with my assailant. She was revealed as a bold-featured woman of about fifty-five with suspiciously black hair framing cheeks plastered one inch thick with rouge. The sharp edge of her Dame Edna glasses pierced my cheek like a nail and, through the lenses, the alcohol meter in her eyes most definitely registered full. She greeted me enthusiastically.

'Thank Christ I never missed you, lad!' she screamed into my ear. 'The bastards round here'll screw the meter as soon as the coffin's carried out.'

I extricated myself carefully from her clutches but she was determined not to lose her prey. She grabbed hold of my wrist and dragged me towards the house.

She squeezed her ample frame past a man standing in the doorway, smearing the shoulder of his jacket with rouge and spilling the contents of his glass. He didn't seem at all bothered.

She turned to speak to him. 'Hey, Eddie, fetch more ale in from the yard! We're down to the last couple of barrels.' Judging by the size of Eddie's stomach, this would probably be a labour of love.

I'd barely got into the house before I was again accosted, this time more gently, by a bespectacled young man of earnest appearance. The crisp whiteness of his dog collar was marred by blotches of rouge. He seized my free hand and shook it energetically. 'Hello, I'm Father Mulcahy. Billy was one of my parishioners, well... er... nominally at least... and you are...?' He looked to my kidnapper for an introduction.

It was very cursory. 'Oh, he's drrelleckyman,' she said without looking at either of us. I was fast becoming the rope in a tug of war. She was trying to pull me up the hall, but the priest still had hold of my hand. He showed no inclination to move away.

'Pleased to meet you, Mr Drekelmann.' He pumped my hand again, 'Yes, it's a sad occasion, but at least he's now at peace.' Listening to the sounds of revelry in the back room, I wasn't so sure. 'Of course he had his faults, but which of us can stand totally pure before the Lord at the Day of Judgement? We all need to rely on His infinite mercy.' He let go of my hand before adding, somewhat incongruously, 'They'll certainly miss Billy at the billiards club.'

Meanwhile, two other guests had approached my hostess to express their condolences, giving me some respite. Both departed heavily stained with rouge.

The pause allowed me to get my bearings. The houses at the bottom end of Bedford Road had their meter cupboards in the cellar. Those in the middle had them in the kitchen. This house was at the top end where the meters were in the parlour just below the window. My heart sank. I knew the coffin would be right in front of it.

Sure enough, Mrs Rouge pushed open the parlour door. I poked my head round gingerly. Smack! A plastic football hit me in the face. Two small boys stood there shamefaced.

Mrs Rouge seemed not to notice. She was more concerned that the candles on the mantelpiece had gone out. 'Aaah, look at that! Billy would've been fifty-eight today. The grandkids have been singing *Happy Birthday* again, God bless 'em!' She relit the candles.

As the boys slipped out of the room, she led me over to the coffin, which was supported on trestles across the width of the bay. The coffin lid was propped against the wall. I tried desperately to avert my eyes but Mrs Rouge was having none of it. She looked down and lifted the veil off Billy's face. It was stained with rouge.

'Alright, Billy?' She looked at him proudly. 'Doesn't he look well? The undertaker did a really good job on him.' Seeing how haggard he looked in his photo on the mantelpiece, I had to agree. He must have been very ill when it was taken.

I was about to offer sympathy when Eddie appeared at my shoulder and planted a glass in my hand. It was full to the brim. 'Here, get this down yer neck, lad.'

'Er, thanks anyway but it's a bit early. I'd better not while –'

Eddie grabbed hold of my elbow and forced the glass to my lips. 'Don't be soft, lad! A drop of whisky never hurt anyone.' He didn't release my arm until the glass was empty.

'Right,' said Mrs Rouge. 'We haven't got all day. You'd better get started. You'll have to squeeze under the coffin. You can count the money in the kitchen.'

I could hardly refuse. I got down on my knees and crawled into the space underneath. Clumsily, I attempted to unfasten the cash box but already the whisky was bouncing off my stomach and rebounding into my skull. As I struggled to focus, I became vaguely aware of some people walking into the room. Then I heard

Eddie's voice.

'Hey, look at the face on that! Quick, throw a coat over it before it frightens Billy!'

It was well after the laughter had subsided that I realised he'd been referring to my backside.

Somehow I managed to get the cash box off the meter and crawl back out. When I stood up the room was spinning violently. Mrs Rouge grabbed me again and this time I was glad of her support. Otherwise I'd probably have collapsed into the coffin.

She pushed her way through to the kitchen, dragging me in her wake, and sat me at a table where a woman in a white pinny patterned with red (rouge stains) was cutting sandwiches. She cleared a space between a bowl of egg mayonnaise and a plate of meat pies.

'Here you are, lad. Ethel'll do you some sarnies if you feel peckish.'

I didn't. The smell of food was making me feel even more unwell and it was touch and go whether I was going to be sick. I started to count the money.

'Would you like a coffee, love?' asked Ethel, who turned out to be Mrs Rouge's more refined sister. That sounded more attractive.

'Yes please. Black, two sugars.' I thought it would be a good antidote to the whisky.

Ethel called through into the hall. 'Eddie, make this gentleman a coffee, will you? Black, two sugars.'

Eddie brought it in a large mug. It was very hot and very sweet and, when I'd drunk it I did feel better. That was, until I heard Eddie giving details of the recipe. 'The secret's masking the taste of the rum and vodka.'

With difficulty I worked out the bill and divvy and staggered back into the front room. I just wanted to replace the box and get out as soon as possible but I couldn't get to the meter. A small group had gathered round the coffin, convulsed with laughter. Billy was lying with a cigar between his lips and a can of lager in his hand.

Eddie, who seemed to be everywhere, was egging him on. 'Go on, Billy lad, one more won't kill you!'

The bereaved wife, meanwhile, was becoming maudlin. 'Ah, look at him! That's how I want to remember him.' Pulling out a hanky, she wiped away a tear and two layers of rouge.

Suddenly Ethel's voice sounded urgently from the hall. 'Gran's here!' The laughter quickly subsided. Eddie hurriedly restored some semblance of respectability to Billy and everyone moved away from the coffin.

A sombre-faced old lady appeared in the doorway. The room went quiet.

Father Mulcahy, peering anxiously through his spectacles, hovered at her shoulder. 'Come through to the back and have a drink, Mrs Lynch!' he entreated.

'Thank you, Father, but I'd prefer to see him first.' She looked frail but her voice was strong, though she was clearly in the grip of a barely suppressed emotion.

The tension in the room was tangible as she walked over to the coffin. She stood for several seconds gazing down at the now peaceful Billy. Mouth quivering, she took Billy's hand and held it in her own.

'What is it, Mum?' Mrs Rouge asked nervously. 'What are you doing?'

Gran let go of Billy's hand. She could obviously contain her emotion no longer. She looked up at Mrs Rouge with a smile of deepest satisfaction. 'Just checking his pulse, dear. I want to make sure the bastard really is dead.'

Mrs Rouge's tears began to flow again. 'Friggin' hell, Mum! Not now.'

Gran was implacable. 'Why not? What's he going to do about it?' She looked down at the coffin contemptuously.

'Come on, Mrs Lynch, naturally you're a bit upset,' said Father Mulcahy, trying to pour holy oil on troubled waters.

'Upset? Why should I be upset? I'm delighted. That swine led my daughter a dog's life for thirty years. Good riddance to him.'

Mrs Rouge sprang to her husband's defence. 'Mum, that's not fair. We did love each other, didn't we Billy?' She looked for confirmation to Billy who remained impassive. 'You know we did!'

This cut no ice with Gran who directed her venom towards the whole room. 'God knows how many fancy women he had, the filthy little sod! His keks were up and down more times than Lewis's lift!'

'Mrs Lynch, I really think...' You had to give the priest credit for trying.

Gran ignored him. 'I suggest you bury him with his flies open. It's what he would have wanted.'

Mrs Rouge was now becoming angry. 'Jesus Christ! Leave it, Mum! Alright, so he had his faults, but he always came home... eventually. And I wasn't exactly a nun meself... was I, Eddie?' For once that man looked discomfited.

Gran clearly didn't subscribe to the custom of not speaking ill of the dead. 'Anything you did, you were driven to it. I don't know how you put up with him. I'd have castrated the dirty fucker long ago.' Satisfied she had delivered a suitable epitaph, Gran graciously allowed Father Mulcahy to escort her through to the back of the house.

Eddie it appeared, did not trust her even now. 'Better stay close to her, Father!' he called after them. 'And don't let her get her hands on anything sharp!'

With Gran's departure, the atmosphere in the room gradually relaxed.

'Get us another gin, Eddie,' asked Mrs Rouge, regaining her composure. She went across to the record player. 'Never mind, Billy love! Don't worry! I'll put on your favourite song.' She started to rummage through the record sleeves.

I took a deep breath and loosened my collar. I wasn't feeling too well, but I only had to replace the cash box. Then I could get the hell out of this madhouse.

With some effort I got down on my knees and crawled back under the coffin. My hand was shaking and the meter kept moving but I somehow managed to do it. Now if I could just get up... no, I really wasn't feeling very well at all. Perhaps if I closed my eyes for a couple of minutes, I'd be alright.

'ONE O'CLOCK, TWO O'CLOCK, THREE O'CLOCK ROCK!' I sat up abruptly, banging my head on the underside of the coffin and dislodging it from one of the trestles. To my horror it slid towards the floor, knocking over the coffin lid which fell right across the record player and smashed it. The coffin landed on its edge, teetered precariously, then toppled over onto its side. Two white spherical objects fell out and rolled across the carpet.

Everything went quiet and for a few seconds nobody moved. It was Eddie who finally broke the tension. 'Alright, who let Gran back in with the carving knife?'

'Feeling a bit better, love?' I was sitting down with Ethel standing over me solicitously. I did feel better, at least physically. The vomit had been cleared up from the carpet though the smell was still pungent in the atmosphere. The coffin had been remounted on the trestles and the billiard balls replaced inside.

'I thought it'd be a nice touch,' Mrs Rouge had explained. 'Give Billy something to do if he gets bored.' I kept a tactful silence about the record player and Billy's favourite record.

'Like another coffee, son?' Ethel asked.

I thought it might help clear my head. 'Yes, please,' I answered quickly. Then I remembered the last one. 'Er... no thanks. I'd better be on my way.'

No such luck. Before I could get up, the funeral cars arrived. Flanked by his cohorts, the undertaker made his entrance, looking a bit like Boris Karloff on a particularly bad day.

This was the cue for another of Eddie's funnies. 'God, look at the gob on him! You'd think he was on his way to a funeral.'

'Ahem.' Father Mulcahy, blinking nervously, tried hard to assert himself. 'I think we should say a short prayer before Billy leaves this house for the last time.' He made the sign of the cross.

Eddie preferred an alternative version. 'Spectacles, testicles, wallet, watch.' On this occasion he had sufficient decorum to make it only half-audible.

Father Mulcahy finished his prayer. 'Dear Lord on high, please be merciful to your servant, Billy. Forgive him his sins and grant him the grace to enjoy everlasting life with You and all the angels and saints in the Kingdom of Heaven. Amen.' He crossed himself again.

Eddie was not convinced, but he tried to let the priest down gently. 'I shouldn't bother if I were you, Father. He's more likely to need asbestos underwear where he's going.'

48

The undertaker asked everyone to leave the room while the coffin was sealed. Mrs Rouge gave Billy one last kiss. Gran, unforgiving to the last, took a more practical view. 'Make sure you do the job properly! He's nearly escaped once already.'

The pallbearers carried out the coffin and placed it securely in the hearse. Behind it the cortege stretched way back down Bedford Road. Billy must have been a very popular character unless, like Gran, they were all making sure he was dead. Mrs Rouge, tearful again, gave me a hug and climbed into the leading car with Eddie and Ethel. The other mourners got into the cars behind.

I watched the procession slowly pull away and breathed a huge sigh of relief. Never had I been so glad to get away from a house. I wiped the rouge off my face and checked the list for my next call.

Suddenly, a hundred yards up the road, the procession stopped. The door of the leading car opened and Mrs Rouge clambered out. What the hell was wrong now? Waving her arms furiously, she began to run back down the road towards me. No! This wasn't really happening. The alcohol was still in my system. I was hallucinating, surely! I closed my eyes for a few seconds. When I opened them again, she was still there, getting nearer and nearer. It was far too late for flight. I stood transfixed.

She arrived, breathless, and grabbed hold of my arm violently. This was becoming eerily reminiscent of our first encounter. I began to shake.

'Thank Christ, lad! I'm glad I caught you in time.'

I looked at her blankly. 'What do you mean?'

'Jesus, with all the excitement it went right out of me head. I nearly forgot me friggin' divvy!'

When at last they had gone, this time finally, finally gone, I thought fleetingly of my own funeral. Would it be a solemn and sedate affair or a more riotous assembly, packed with colour and controversy like Billy's? I didn't know which I'd prefer but of one thing I was certain. I didn't want it gatecrashed, however inadvertently, by some poor sap who'd only come to empty a meter.

THRONE ALONE

Red Lenny had two great claims to fame amongst the Manweb workforce. One was his unswerving support for the rights of the downtrodden worker against the lackeys of capitalist imperialism; the other was the legendary nature of his bowel movements.

These bowel movements weren't just natural bodily functions, they were social occasions. Anyone walking into the toilet would be summoned to Lenny's cubicle door to discuss the issues of the day, debate some abstruse political point or help him finish off a crossword. As shop steward, Lenny often conducted delicate industrial negotiations through an inch of chipboard and melamine. However, Lenny's most celebrated bowel movement coincided with a very different sort of evacuation.

I was listening to Radio Merseyside early one morning when I first heard the news. It was the lead item. *There has been a huge explosion at Mersey House in Bootle. The block has now been evacuated. At the moment there are unconfirmed reports of one casualty.*

I was already late so, as is the way with human nature, I soon forgot about other people's misfortunes and continued getting ready for work.

I was still ten minutes late when I arrived at Derby House. Tentatively I opened the door of Tommy's office, steeling myself for the sarcasm habitually reserved for latecomers. But this time I needn't have bothered. Some of the collectors were sitting in front of a blackboard on which were drawn half a dozen matchstick men and a tall rectangle listing to one side like the Tower of Pisa. Alongside the blackboard stood Tommy, holding a stick and looking very important. No one took any notice of me as I slipped into a vacant chair.

'Right, now pay attention, men.' Tommy, chest out and stomach in, was clearly in his element. 'The reputation of the reg – er, the company is at stake here. At approximately 06:00 hours this morning the bottom floor of Mersey House in Bootle was blown up as a result of enemy action – I mean a gas explosion,' he corrected himself hastily. 'The fire brigade has evacuated the building. The police have now asked us to go in and empty all the meters before looters do it for us.'

Big Ron looked worried. 'Stuff this for a game of soldiers,' he muttered under his breath. 'I don't fancy getting killed just to make Tommy a hero.'

Tommy silenced him with a glare. 'Now, listen carefully. We shall take three, repeat three, vans and travel in convoy. I will drive the first van, Morris will drive the second, Brennan will drive the third. Make sure you all keep together. When we arrive at our target,'– he tapped the Tower of Pisa with his stick – 'I will assess the situation and act accordingly. Take no orders from anyone but me! I shall be the officer in command. Now, synchronise watches! It is now nine twenty five and... thirty seconds precisely. Right, follow me!' He turned and marched out of the room.

None of us moved. Within seconds Tommy marched back in again. 'What the bloody hell do you lot think you're doing? You're supposed to be coming with me.'

Lenny stood up. 'Hang on a minute.' He extracted a book from the top pocket of his jacket. 'As I'm sure you're aware, according to rule 3, subsection 2a, no collector may be compelled to enter a premises if he deems his personal safety to be compromised in any way, whether it be due to the unsafe structure of such premises or potentially violent behaviour of the occupants therein. My members cannot be expected to expose their persons to danger without some token additional remuneration.' He looked challengingly at Tommy.

I expected Tommy to explode much as Mersey House had done but he took it philosophically. 'Suit yourselves,' he said, shrugging his shoulders, 'but if the looters do get in, the company's going to lose a lot of money. That could mean no more overtime for at least six months.' He shook his head sadly. 'Still, no-one's forcing you. It's your decision.' He walked back out of the office. This time we followed him to a man.

Outside Mersey House things had happened very quickly. In the four hours since the explosion all hundred and forty-odd flats had been evacuated, their tenants ferried off to churches, school halls, sports centres and other temporary shelters. The stricken block had been cordoned off with wire fencing and police had set up a mobile incident room a safe distance away. Groups of policemen, firemen and engineers stood huddled deep in discussion while a TV camera filmed from across the road. Further off, clusters of spectators looked on curiously.

Tommy screeched to a halt behind three fire engines and a police car. He jumped out of the van, looked over at the camera, straightened his cap, set his jaw and surveyed the scene thoughtfully like a tough jungle veteran scanning the foliage for hidden danger. A police sergeant emerged from the incident room and walked over to greet him.

Tommy thrust out his hand. 'Good morning. I'm ex-Sergeant Greenwood, head of the Manweb special unit. Your CO's called us in case of looting. We got here as quickly as we could.'

'Jolly good,' the policeman replied, ignoring Tommy's proffered handshake, 'but you'd better move those vans sharpish. This is for emergency vehicles only.'

Tommy's sense of importance was badly deflated. 'Jumped up little prat! I thought we were emergency vehicles,' he muttered darkly as he drove a further hundred and fifty yards up the road. 'Honestly! You give some of these buggers a uniform and they think they're it!' I could detect no conscious sense of irony in his voice.

However, the Chief Fire Officer managed to smooth Tommy's ruffled feathers. 'Good of you to come at such short notice, Mr Greenwood. We're really very grateful.'

Tommy waved this away airily. Who cared about such social niceties at time of crisis?

'We've enough problems as it is without having to worry about looters,' continued the Fire Chief. He looked over at the damaged block. 'I'll tell you one thing. It's an absolute miracle no-one's been killed.'

It was difficult not to agree. At the front, every window in the first five storeys had been blown out, leaving broken glass strewn everywhere. An ominously large crack embellished the outer wall of the caretaker's flat on the ground floor, where the explosion had occurred. The caretaker himself had been incredibly lucky. Apparently he had struck a match in his kitchen, unaware that the gas pipe leading to his cooker had fractured. Seconds later he was sitting outside on the grass, badly singed and deeply shocked but otherwise unhurt. He was still clutching an unlit cigarette.

'I'll leave you to sort your men out,' said the Fire Chief. He pointed to a gap in the fencing outside the front entrance to the building where two other firemen were at a table perusing lists of names. 'You can pick up the hard hats over there. Make sure everyone signs the sheet before you go in and don't forget to leave names and addresses of your next of kin. Good luck!'

Tommy's jaw suddenly slackened. ' Next of kin? Surely you don't need to know our next of kin!'

The Fire Chief looked him squarely in the eye. 'To tell the truth we can't be sure how much the structure's been weakened by the explosion. There's an outside chance it could collapse. That's what happened in Kuala Lumpur a couple of years ago. Six hours after the explosion the whole block suddenly caved in like a house of cards. God forbid that should happen here but, if it does, we may need next of kin to identify the bodies.'

Tommy swallowed hard. He digested this information for a few seconds, then suddenly made up his mind. 'OK, men. There's nothing else for it. We've got a job to do. We'll take two floors each. We'll start from the upper of the two floors at the rear of the building and work through to the front end of the lower floor. Morris, you take ground and first floor, Griffiths, second and third, Reeves, fourth and fifth, Brennan, six and seven, Cowhig, eight and nine, Redwood, ten and eleven, Smith, twelve and thirteen, Kelly, fourteen and fifteen, Taylor sixteen and seventeen. We'll have to use the stairs of course because the power's off. When you're done, meet me down here and await further instructions. Any questions?'

Red Lenny raised his hand. 'Just one thing, boss.'

'Yes Redwood?'

'Aren't you coming in with us?'

Tommy looked at him witheringly. 'Come on, lad, don't be stupid! Someone has to stay out here and co-ordinate.'

'Not so fast!'

We'd registered our names and next of kin, put on our hard hats and were just about to enter the building when we were forestalled by a shout. It was Tommy's favourite policeman. 'I'm afraid you can't go in on your own. Each collector will have to be accompanied by a police officer.'

Tommy glared at him. 'Why?'

'It's merely a precaution, sir. Just in case anything goes missing.'

Tommy bristled with indignation. 'Are you suggesting my men are not to be trusted?' he demanded. This was rich considering he had often suggested the same thing himself.

'Not at all, sir,' the sergeant answered calmly. 'It's for their own protection. In case any of the flats are subsequently broken into before the tenants return. My officers are witnesses to the fact that you've only emptied the meters.'

'Hmm.' Tommy no doubt saw the logic of this but could not entirely forget the slight over parking spaces. 'That's all very well, but who's going to keep an eye on your policemen?'

Following Tommy's instructions I started work on the ninth floor. As I moved from flat to flat, it was an eerie sensation. Doors had been left open, radios were blaring out, budgies were twittering unconcernedly in their cages. Everything was quite normal except that the place was deserted.

'Must have been like this on the *Marie Celeste*,' I remarked to the policeman with me but he stared stonily ahead, ignoring me. Just my luck, I thought bitterly, to be lumbered with the most miserable copper on Merseyside!

It happened suddenly, without warning. 'Can't breathe!... Can't breathe!... Open the window!' gasped my companion, pulling frantically to loosen his collar. I did as he asked and he slumped against the windowsill, sucking in great gulps of air. Trembling visibly, he clung to the sill for two or three minutes, not daring to look down. I did and couldn't believe my eyes. There was Tommy, right arm aloft, creeping round behind the sergeant and stabbing him swiftly in the back. I knew he'd got up Tommy's nose but this was ridiculous. Then the penny dropped. Tommy had found a virgin audience for his jungle exploits.

The policeman's breathing soon got easier. 'Sorry about that,' he said looking deeply embarrassed. 'I thought I could feel the building move.' He paused, then added tentatively, 'I'd appreciate it if you didn't say anything to the others.'

It took us another forty-five minutes to finish the job. Two of the meters I couldn't empty because they'd already been broken open, the tenants assuming the theft could never be traced back to them. How sad that, even in the midst of peril, human greed prevailed! Still, at least it proved the sergeant had been right to send his men in with us.

Our names were ticked off as we emerged from the building like soldiers at the end of a mission. 'Anything to report?' Tommy asked. I shook my head. There was only the panic attack and the policeman's secret was safe with me. Two more collectors and their escorts appeared and joined us. 'Well done, lads,' said Tommy. 'Now gather round! I want to debrief you.'

Big Ron couldn't resist the opportunity. 'No offence, boss, but I'd rather have a pat on the back if it's all the same with you.'

Before Tommy could snarl a reply, one of the firemen spoke up. 'There's two still inside, you know. Constable Jackson and Leonard Redwood. Surely they should be finished by now.'

Tommy sighed loudly. 'Red bloody Lenny! That bugger's more trouble than he's worth.' He looked at his watch. 'Give him a couple more minutes. He's probably trying to start the flippin' revolution.'

We waited, with growing unease, for several minutes but there was still no sign of Lenny or Constable Jackson. Even Tommy, beneath his growing irritation, showed traces of concern. Finally, there was no choice but to go in after them. Tommy grabbed a hard hat. No-one dared ask him for his next of kin.

Five of us were deputed for the search party. Tommy and the police sergeant for the tenth floor, Big Ron, one of the fireman and myself for the eleventh. We set off up the stairs only to meet Constable Jackson, looking apprehensive, on his way down. He led us back up to the tenth floor, down a corridor and into one of the flats. He stopped outside the toilet door. 'He's been in there ages. I think he's trapped.'

Tommy banged hard on the door. 'Lenny, what's up? Come on out!' There was no reply. 'Are you all right in there?'

Lenny's voice came from within. 'The lock's broken.'

'Maybe the building's moved,' suggested Constable Jackson nervously. 'Could've thrown the locks out of alignment.'

Tommy scratched his head. 'Suppose we could break the door down.' – he looked at the firemen questioningly – 'as long as it doesn't destabilise the whole structure.'

'I've got an axe downstairs,' said the fireman. 'I'll go and fetch it. He disappeared down the corridor.'

Tommy shook his head in exasperation. 'We're just going for help, Lenny, so don't worry!'

Lenny's voice rang out again. 'The lock's broken.'

'I know that,' said Tommy, 'but we'll soon have you out. Don't panic!'

'The lock's broken,' Lenny said for the third time.

'Poor bastard's getting delirious,' Tommy whispered to the sergeant. 'Bloody younger generation! None of 'em have got any bottle.' He put his head closer to the door. 'Just stay calm, Lenny. You're in good hands. There's nothing to worry about.'

It was Ron who was first to realise the true situation. He'd been down that road many times before. 'How many letters, Lenny?'

'Two words. Five and four. S, blank, L, blank, T. Blank, N, blank, S.'

Ron thought for some moments, his brow furrowed. '*Split ends*' he said finally. There was silence from inside the toilet. 'You know... the locks broken... locks of hair... *split ends*.'

'Of course. Thanks, Ron.' I could imagine Lenny writing in the answer.

Tommy meanwhile had turned puce. 'I really don't believe this! I'm standing out here moments from death with half the bleedin' emergency services on Merseyside and soft lad's sitting on the toilet doing a friggin' crossword!' Forgetting the building's potential instability, he punched the toilet door.

'I've been struggling over this one for ages,' said the voice inside the toilet, ignoring him. 'Four words. Diarrhoea is hereditary. Question mark.'

'How many letters, Lenny?' asked Ron.

'Four, two, three, six. First word begins with *r*. I think the third word's *the*... and the second word must be *in* or *it*.'

If Tommy ever did have time for the puzzler's art (which was unlikely), this wasn't it. 'Listen here, Redwood! I'm not hanging round risking life and limb while you're in there playing silly buggers. Get off that friggin' toilet now or you're sacked!' It was the wrong thing to say.

'You have no grounds for a sacking or indeed any other form of disciplinary action.' There was a rustle from inside the toilet, which could have been, but probably wasn't, Lenny putting down his newspaper and thumbing through the union rule book. It was more likely he was making it all up. 'Any member of the workforce is entitled to toilet breaks not exceeding thirty minutes in total during any one session, each working day consisting of two sessions – a.m. and p.m. The member himself shall be the sole arbiter of when and where such breaks shall be required. This is especially true when the member is exposed to physical danger, which may interfere with his or her normal bowel or bladder functions. Rule 8b, subsection 4. Any attempt to interfere with this process would be legitimate grounds for industrial action and should be reported.'

Tommy banged on the door again. 'You bastard! You're only doing this because I wouldn't give you danger money, aren't you?' There was a plop from inside the toilet, then silence. Tommy knew when he was beaten. 'Right you've got five minutes. If you're not out by then, make your own friggin' way home!' He tapped his watch pointedly. Behind his back a small smile flickered across the sergeant's face.

Tommy stood glaring impotently at the toilet door, ignoring the return of the fireman with his axe. After five minutes exactly the cistern flushed and Lenny emerged, dignified, his newspaper neatly folded under his arm. He smiled politely at Tommy. 'Shall we go?' I could swear Tommy almost made a grab for the axe.

Back outside Tommy vented his feelings strongly to the Chief Fire Officer. 'To think I spent four years fighting in the jungle for people like him. Bloody Commie! His father used to work here before him. He was just the same. Another bloody troublemaker. It obviously runs in the family.'

Lenny clapped his hand ostentatiously to his forehead. 'That's it! Thank you, Tommy!' he exclaimed, taking his pen from his top pocket.

Tommy couldn't bring himself to address Lenny directly. 'What's that stupid pillock on about now?' he muttered.

Lenny chose not to take offence. 'That crossword clue. You've just solved it for me. Well done!'

Tommy responded despite himself. 'Crossword clue? What the bloody hell are you talking about, Redwood?'

Lenny held the paper out in front of Tommy. 'You know, that clue we couldn't get before. Diarrhoea is hereditary? Four, two, three, six. You've just answered it – *runs in the family.'*

The tenants of Mersey House returned the following day to collect essential belongings but it was six weeks before they could finally move back in. As for Tommy, unusually, he didn't appear for work the following morning. By coincidence, it was Lenny who took the call.

'Hello, it's Mrs Greenwood here. My husband won't be in till this afternoon. I've just sent him to the doctor's. I know he's a bit odd at the best of times but now he's really flipped. He was up half the night shouting at the toilet door.'

THE CHINESE SIDEBOARD

The huge council estates of Kirkby do not normally evoke images of forbidden oriental romance. However, this all changed for me after one never-to-be-forgotten visit.

I had just finished my day's work at Cherryfield Heights, an ugly high-rise block of flats that should never have been built, when the caretaker called me over. 'Sorry about this, pal, but the old lady in number 87 just asked me if you'd called to her flat.' 87 was on the top floor and checking my card I saw she was down as a *no reply*.

'Alright,' I said, 'I'll go back up. I don't suppose she puts much in her meter.' A lot of old people had been conditioned by a lifetime of hardship and most of them used electricity sparingly. There was never usually very much in their meters. I was sure I'd be in and out in a couple of minutes.

The air was heavy with the smell of urine and graffiti was daubed everywhere. *LFC* and *EFC* fought with *Bassa is Boss* and *JL loves TH* for prominence on the walls. I entered the lift and pressed the button for the top floor. In the confined space the smell was even stronger. *JL* had been busy here too, this time proclaiming his love for *PR*. I hoped *TH* would not be too upset.

The lift doors opened just as the stench was making me feel sick. The door to 87 was open and a little old lady stood waiting for me.

'Are you the electric man?' She spoke with a perfectly modulated, almost aristocratic, accent.

'Yes, love,' I answered. 'You were out when I called before.' I followed her up the hall and into a sad but beautiful story.

The flat was small and sparsely furnished. However, the main wall of her living room was dominated by an ornate oriental sideboard with legs intricately carved in the shape of dragons. Its curved drawers were inlaid with gold leaf. On top of the sideboard were four pictures. Three showed a group of Chinese, clad in long black coats, with a European couple in the foreground. The fourth picture was of two young women, one European and one Chinese, smiling and linking arms.

The old lady's name was Joanna Wright and she was eighty-six years old. Although she was frail, her movements were balanced and steady but the most distinctive thing about her was her voice. It resembled that of an early BBC announcer and seemed quite out of place in Kirkby. In some ways she reminded me of the Queen Mother.

I counted the money from her meter while she made some tea. When I'd finished working out her bill, I sat back and glanced across at the sideboard. 'That's a beautiful piece of furniture. I've never seen anything like it.'

Her face lit up. 'It's unique. I had it made to my own design.' My curiosity was getting the better of me and for the next hour I sat and listened to the fascinating story of her life.

Joanna Barlow was born in Liverpool in 1894 and spent the early part of her life in Aigburth. Her father was a shipping manager for Lamport and Holt, who had prestigious offices in the Liver Building overlooking the waterfront. She had one sister who died of TB when Joanna was ten. Her mother died the following year of the same disease. When she was eighteen she met her husband, Captain Charles Wright of the King's (Liverpool) Regiment. He was twenty-seven.

'I met him by Sefton Park boating lake. He asked me to look after his coat while he took his shoes and socks off. His model boat was stuck in the middle of the lake.' As she told me her story I noticed she had the clear blue eyes of a much younger woman. 'He thanked me, then off he went.'

She opened a drawer in the sideboard and took out a picture of Charles. He had a thin, fine-boned face with large intelligent eyes and resembled an old Hollywood movie star whose name I couldn't remember. He looked very distinguished in his army uniform.

'After that, I met him several times walking through the park. Then one day he asked me to marry him. We hadn't even kissed. Before I knew it I was married and travelling on a slow boat to China.' Captain Wright had been posted to Shanghai as a military attaché and Far East Observer to the British Army.

'We lived in a ten-bedroom colonial house in the international part of the city. When we arrived, three maids came out to meet us. The house had a massive garden with its own lake so Charles could sail his boats to his heart's content.'

Three or four times I stood up to go but I couldn't. I'd been shanghaied (in the nicest possible way) by her story.

She took out another photograph from the drawer. 'All these people belonged to Shanghai's high society. The man sitting next to me taught me to speak Chinese.'

My face betrayed my surprise. 'You can speak Chinese?'

'Of course I can. There are dozens of different dialects. I can speak Mandarin – that's the language used by government officials – and Shanghai street dialect, which the ordinary people speak. And I can speak French as well.' From the sideboard she took the picture of the two women and polished it before handing it to me.

'That's me and my best friend. Her name was Li Meiying and she was the head maid to the house. It was her father who made the sideboard. He was a cabinet maker.'

I looked closely at the picture and saw two happy, smiling women. Both were very young and pretty.

'Mei told me that if you ever felt sad, then you should find a tree and make it your friend. Tell it all your problems. You can always trust a tree. It won't tell a soul about your secrets and you'll feel better for talking to it.' Her head was tilted to one side as if she was listening to someone in the distance. Then she laughed. 'I've got my own tree to talk to now.' She stood up and walked over to the window. 'Look over there! By that wall there's a little tree. It knows all my secrets.'

I followed her over to the window. Alongside the flats was a large field. On the far side, close to a brick wall, stood a small apple tree covered in beautiful white blossom. Joanna said she sat there most days and talked to it.

'I sometimes feel Mei is still here with me.' She remained a few moments, gazing at the tree in silence.

'When the Great War came in 1914, Charles was recalled to his regiment. I followed him and joined the Nursing Corps. It was terrible! All those young boys, so many of them! I took my faith in God to France and left it there.' She looked down at the floor. I imagined she could see all kinds of nightmares from the field hospitals of Flanders.

'Charles survived the war. He was one of the lucky ones. Most of his friends were killed or mutilated. Afterwards, he was posted back to Shanghai. Mei said I was different and that it would take the biggest forest in the world to help me with my problems now. I never told her what I saw in those field hospitals. I didn't have to. She could see it in my face. Sometimes, when the nightmares came looking for me, Mei would hold me long into the night.'

Joanna went off to make another pot of tea. On her return she took up the story again.

'Charles was always off somewhere doing army work, so Mei and I would have a right old time.' She giggled at the memory like a young schoolgirl. Then her expression became sad again. 'You know, when I told Mei how I first met Charles by the boating lake, she said nothing had changed. I would always be standing on the side watching him splash about. I never jumped in to join him.

'Then one day Charles came home and said he was leaving the army and going into business. He began to export fine art and porcelain to places all over the world. We had to move out of the army house so Charles leased an apartment in the Chinese area of the city. Mei came with us as housekeeper and we brought the sideboard too.'

'Didn't you ever feel homesick?' I asked.

Joanna shook her head. 'No, I was very happy there. It was the best time of my life.'

'You must've missed your family though.'

'Not really. My father had died and Charles's family never acknowledged me anyway. They were against the marriage from the start. They thought he'd married beneath him. Whenever we came back to England, I would stay in a hotel while he visited them. The last time we came back, Charles let me bring Mei with me.' She gave a mischievous smile.

'Just after we set sail for China, Charles was taken ill. It was an old war wound. He'd gone down at the battle of the Somme with appendicitis of all things. For a couple of years he'd complained about a pain in his side. Too much work and too much whisky, I used to tell him. I was wrong. Apparently when the doctors had operated on him, they'd left a scalpel in his stomach. Mei and I nursed him as best we could, but he died just as we docked in Cape Town. Quite ironic, really. The enemy didn't get him but his own side did. Seems he wasn't so lucky after all.

'I wired to Shanghai for money. It was then I found out his business had collapsed. His family wouldn't help so we buried him in Cape Town. We had no choice. We couldn't afford anything else. I've never been able to visit his grave since.'

I looked at Joanna, not quite knowing what to say.

'That's not all. While we were away, the Japanese had invaded Shanghai. That was in 1932. I'll never forget that year.'

I felt as if I was watching a drama unfold before me.

'When we arrived back we couldn't get to the apartment. The city had been cordoned off and we were told to stay in the international zone. I wanted to retrieve my belongings, but we risked being shot dead if we stepped outside the designated sector. Mei said she would try and get some friends to help.

'She went out the next morning and never came back. I grew more and more worried. That night a young man called to the rooms where I was staying. I followed him outside and he pointed to the sideboard on a handcart. I asked him about Mei. He lowered his eyes and said the Japanese had shot her in the street outside the apartment.' Joanna looked directly ahead as she spoke, transported to another world in another age. She gestured towards the photographs on the sideboard. 'All those people were shot by the Japanese. I often go back there in my mind. I think of being with Mei when she was shot and both of us dying together. But then, that didn't happen, did it?'

I shook my head. 'No, it didn't.'

'I came back to England soon afterwards. All I had to show for my life was a sideboard and a few photographs. Fortunately, I was able to get a job nursing at the Royal Infirmary. Over the years, I tried very hard to find God again but He was still in France.' She got up to make yet another pot of tea. I tried to tell her I had to go, but I couldn't tear myself away from her story.

'I dedicated my life to caring for people who were suffering. When you just look at a person... any person... you don't know what they've been through... you don't know how much they've suffered, do you?'

'No, I said, 'you don't.' It was something I'd never thought about before.

'Oddly enough, the sideboard saved my life during the May Blitz. The nearest air-raid shelter to where I was living was at the end of the street. I couldn't be bothered running down there, so I used to lie under the sideboard. I suppose you think I'm going to say the house was bombed and the big old sideboard protected me but it wasn't that at all. One night, the air-raid shelter took a direct hit and everyone in it was killed. So, you see, if I hadn't felt so safe under the sideboard, I would have been there and I wouldn't be talking to you now.

'When the war was over, I retired from nursing. I tried one more time to find God but He was gone forever.

'I had a lovely little house just by the John Bagot Hospital in Everton. The Luftwaffe missed it, but the council didn't. But then, if they hadn't knocked it down, I wouldn't have come here and found my precious little tree, would I?'

There was so much more Joanna could have told me and there were so many questions I wanted to ask, but this time I really did have to go.

'I loved Mei so much, you know. I still miss her every day. I look at that sideboard and cry, remembering how she died for the sake of a silly old piece of furniture. Then I think, maybe she knew that it would look after me and one day it would save my life.' I noticed she remembered Mei with a much deeper affection than she did Charles. It was only then that I understood her knowing little smile and just how close her relationship with Mei had been. Some pennies take a long time to drop.

As I turned to take my leave, she pushed two pound notes into my hand. 'Thanks for letting a silly old woman relive a few memories. Have a couple of drinks on Mei and me.' She gave me a quick wink and a smile.

'Take care of yourself, Mrs Wright,' I said after thanking her, 'I'll see you next time.' I said something similar to every customer, but this time I really meant it. On the lift door I noticed *JL* had transferred his affections to *YS* and realised I was back in a world much shallower than the one I'd just left. I sensed Joanna would have preferred to die on the street with Mei.

It was another six months before I returned to Cherryfield Heights. When I reached the top floor, number 87 was vacant. I went down to the caretaker, fully expecting him to tell me Joanna had passed away. He didn't.

'I've no idea what happened to her,' he said. 'The flat was empty when I came back off holiday. Even the council doesn't know where she's gone. She just disappeared.'

As I walked back to the van, I glanced across the field towards Joanna's tree. To my surprise that too had gone. To this day nobody knows what became of Joanna and her little apple tree of secrets. But should you ever come across an old sideboard with dragon's legs and curved drawers inlaid with gold, then take good care of it. There's only one like it in the world.

FLUFFY COME HOME

I often used to be amused by the incongruous names people sometimes gave their pets. In the course of my travels I came across a rottweiler called Fifi, a canary called Rover and a goldfish called Brains. And then, of course, there was Fluffy.

One afternoon I called at a house close by Smithdown Road. The front door was open and, as I looked up the hall, I could see the carpet pulled back and a number of floorboards up. The legs and torso of a man were visible.
'Fluffy, come to Daddy!' said the torso. 'Come on, boy! Daddy's waiting to give you your dinner.'
'Hello, I've come to empty the meter,' I called.
'It's behind the door,' came the muffled reply from below. 'You can empty it on the coffee table in the front room.'
Fluffy was probably a little kitten but you could never be sure. Gingerly, I opened the cupboard door and was relieved to find nothing more threatening than the standard dual-coin Ferranti slot meter.
Daddy was now trying to tempt Fluffy with 'a nice big cuddle.' I stepped over him and carried the cash box into the front room where a small boy and girl were kneeling with their heads halfway up the chimney.
'Fluffy, Fluffy, come down!' they called. Both looked really worried. They gave me only a cursory glance as I sat on the sofa to empty the cashbox. I guessed if Fluffy was up there, they'd probably need to change his name to Sooty.
In the bay window was a huge glass tank. There was no water in it but it had sand on the bottom and a large branch running across its width. Before I had a chance to consider its significance, a woman came into the room and joined the children at the chimney.
'Fluffy! Mummy wants you!' she shouted, but to no avail. She straightened up again. 'Poor little sod! I hope he hasn't got outside. God knows what'll happen if the local dogs get hold of him.' That settled it – Fluffy was a kitten. From the way they were fussing, he was probably only a few weeks old.
I couldn't have been more wrong.
Mummy looked across and spotted me on the sofa. 'Hey, lad, you haven't seen a snake on your travels, have you?'
I felt my bowels disintegrate. *Snake...* did she say... *snake*? Or was it *snack*? That's right, she must have been offering me a snack... with fluffy pastry. Liverpool people were always very hospitable. There was nothing to worry about. The snack wouldn't kill me... no, but the bloody snake would!
Daddy reappeared. 'Alright lad, everything OK?' This was a standard enquiry to which I usually responded automatically. But not this time. Everything most

certainly was not OK.

'H... h. . . how l... l... long has the s... s... snack... er... snake been m... missing?' I asked in my best soprano.

'We haven't seen him all day. Suppose we'll have to warn the whole street in case he comes up one of their toilets.' I was grateful for the warning. I certainly wouldn't be using any lavatories in that neighbourhood for a while.

Hurriedly, I counted the money. Mummy signed for her divvy and gave me a two pound tip. Politeness struggled with an overwhelming desire to get the hell out of it.

'H... how b... big is he?' I found myself asking.

'He's an eight foot python.' Daddy grinned with pride as he spoke.

Suddenly the whole front room begun to sink before my eyes. I could feel an earthquake vibrating through the sofa. Then, to my horror, I realised that it wasn't the house sinking but me rising. What happened next still gives me nightmares.

The whole family gasped as an evil head with a sharp, flickering tongue eased its way out from between my legs. I froze.

Mummy at least was pleased to see him. 'Fluffy, you little pest! You were in the settee all the time.' She leapt forward to embrace him. As the snake oozed further out into the room, Daddy hugged him lovingly round the middle.

'Fluffy!' sang the children, fighting to grab his tail. 'You've come back.'

As the last part of the creature flopped to the floor, I felt I'd given birth. Exhausted with fear, I fell back onto the settee. Oblivious to my distress, Fluffy's forgiving family continued to smother him with kisses. I hardly noticed when the lid was lifted off the tank and the snake put back inside.

'Poor little chap, he must be starving.' Daddy said.

'Can I get him his dinner, dad?' asked the small boy eagerly.

'Yes, OK, but don't mess with them!' he warned. *Them*? Why *them*? How can dinner be called *them*? I suppose it should have been obvious, but fear had traumatised my brain.

The boy returned excitedly carrying a small metal cage. Inside were four rats, all running round in panic. This was *them*. I had to get out. Not that I begrudged the runaway his dinner, but I was in no mood to watch him eat.

I was too slow. The rats were tossed into the tank. Fluffy seized one in mid air, swallowing it in one gulp. Two others quickly followed. The last rat had managed to hide at the base of the branch. As it sat trembling, I knew how it felt. Desperate for fresh air, I ran out of the room.

This was a mistake. In my panic I'd forgotten the floorboards in the hall were up. My legs vanished as I plummeted down into the bowels of the house and landed with a jarring thud on my bottom. Worse was to follow. As I writhed around in agony, two sharp fangs bit smartly into my buttock and something long and rubbery coiled itself around my ankle. I nearly passed out. My God, did these weirdos keep

a nest of bloody pythons under the floorboards?

The lights began to flicker as if in a scene from a low-budget horror movie. My heart was pounding so loudly it must have been audible back at the depot. Desperately, I fought to free myself from the snake's evil clutches. But I knew it was in vain. My chest began to tighten. I couldn't breathe. This was it, my life sacrificed in the cause of duty, the first collector to be killed in action. No doubt Tommy would be proud of me, but that wasn't much consolation.

I don't know how much time elapsed before Daddy's face loomed above me. 'Hey, pal, mind that bleedin' cable! You'll fuse all the soddin' lights at this rate.'

Back above ground, I inspected the damage. Embarrassed, I removed the two rusty nails from my bottom with as much dignity as I could muster – which wasn't a lot – and staggered gratefully out into the street.

Six months later I asked Tommy if someone else could empty Fluffy's meter. Since there were no volunteers, he was adamant that I had to do it. When I arrived, I couldn't believe it. The floorboards were still up in the hall.

This time Daddy was sitting on the stairs reading a book. 'You can empty the meter in the front room,' he said as before. He never removed his eyes from the book as he spoke.

I walked nervously through into the front room. The tank was empty and the children were sitting in the fireplace. The soprano voice returned.

'Has Fluffy escaped again?' I asked, beginning to tremble uncontrollably.

'We haven't got Fluffy any more,' came the reply. Thank God! A surge of relief swept over me. Happy and relaxed, I started to count the cash out of the meter.

Suddenly the girl leaned forward and shouted up the chimney. 'Eddie, are you up there? Eddie, come down!'

I didn't dare ask. I didn't really want to find out.

Just then Daddy walked in and tossed the book he was reading onto the settee. 'I don't know! Poor little Eddie could be anywhere.'

My eyes opened wide in horror as I caught sight of the words on its cover: *The Fascinating World of Tarantulas*.

A BITE BELOW THE BELT

'You'll be alright lad, he's only being friendly!' came the traditional words of reassurance. Seconds later the huge pit bull terrier sank its teeth deep into my testicles. Screaming, I staggered backwards into the front room with the dog fastened securely to my groin. The owner tried to rescue me by grabbing hold of the dog's back legs and pulling hard. Desperate to preserve the family crown jewels, I grabbed its head and pulled in the opposite direction. The result was stalemate.

The owner's wife came into the front room with a screwdriver and stood over us. Everything was still, almost unreal. The pit bull was lying beneath me, its jaws clamped between my legs. Like most dogs, once it had a ball in its mouth it was reluctant to let go. My whole body was bathed in sweat.

'Try and keep still,' said the woman as she wedged the screwdriver into the dog's mouth. Her advice was unnecessary – I wasn't thinking of going anywhere just yet. Slowly, she prised the dog's teeth apart, loosening its vice-like grip. As soon as the pressure was relieved, a new wave of pain surged through my body. She grabbed the dog's head before it could take a second bite and forced the screwdriver more firmly into its mouth. 'Get out quick!' she said urgently, still breathing heavily from the struggle. 'I don't know how much longer I can hold him.'

I didn't need to be told twice. I half-sprinted, half-hobbled down the hallway, looking anxiously over my shoulder in case the dog fancied a second course. By the time I got outside the pain had grown worse. I was a little boy again, feeling very sorry for myself. For a few seconds I wanted my mother to be there, to take me in her arms and comfort me. That is, until I remembered what she always said when I hurt myself as a child:

'Run it under the tap or it'll turn into a pig's foot in the morning!'

I hardly dared to look down at the damage but I could feel blood streaming steadily down my leg. I knew I needed medical treatment and quickly. I'd always been terrified of hospitals but now I had no choice. Clutching my groin, I limped to the nearest bus stop. And as if things weren't already bad enough, I was suddenly seized by a new fear. What would those bastards back at the depot say when they found out where I'd been bitten? Mogsy, Ace, Big Ron and the others – they'd never let me hear the end of it. I could just picture it: handbags left on my desk, brochures for gender realignment pinned on my locker, Tommy showing me his war wound and telling me, 'It's only a scratch'. I was tempted to walk back to the house and let the bloody dog finish me off.

It seemed an eternity, but was probably only five minutes, before the bus came. The doors opened and I carefully manoeuvred myself on board.

'Blimey, you alright, mate? What happened?' said the driver, looking down at my torn and bloodstained trousers. I told him all the gory details. 'Jesus, that sounds nasty! Sit down there by the door. I'll put my foot down.'

He was as good as his word. The bus fairly rattled along, not stopping unless someone wanted to get off. If no-one did, he drove straight past the stops, oblivious to anyone who was waiting. To him, as well as to me, this was a genuine emergency.

We reached Walton Hospital in double quick time. I was just about to get off when I remembered I hadn't paid my fare. I felt painfully inside my pocket. 'How much is that?'

'Don't worry about that, mate. It's on me.' He cut short my thanks. 'You've got more important things to worry about. Best of luck.' There are times in life when you know you've met a real friend. This driver was a truly caring person. I only wished he could have parked his bus and come in with me.

'What is the nature of your injury?' The nurse peered grim-faced over her glasses as she waited for my answer.

'I've been bitten in the groin,' I whispered. I was being ultra-cautious. It was very unlikely anyone from the depot would be there, but I was taking no chances.

'Did you come here by car, ambulance or other.' This was her seventh question. She was ticking off my replies on a large sheet.

'By other,' I said, feeling a little dizzy. I wanted to sit down.

'What mode of transport did you use?'

By now I was becoming annoyed. Did all this really matter? My manhood was hanging by a thread and all she wanted to do was complete a transport survey!

'By bus.'

She ticked a box on the form. 'And what is your religion, sir?' Her pen was poised to make another tick.

'I don't know. I haven't checked the damage yet. I started the day as a Roman Catholic, but now I'm probably Jewish.'

She gave not the trace of a smile. 'I'll put down Roman Catholic, shall I?' I nodded. 'Right, one more question. Have you passed water since you received your injury?'

In retrospect this was probably a sensible question but I was in no mood to be charitable. 'Yes,' I said. 'The bus went over the Leeds-Liverpool Canal.'

Her face remained set in concrete as she handed me a urine bottle. 'Provide a sample if you can. Then take a seat in the waiting room till a doctor can see you.'

I found a toilet and, while doing my best to oblige, nervously inspected the damage. It was not a pretty sight. Nothing appeared to be missing but the whole area was grotesquely swollen and discoloured. The bleeding had stopped but two holes in my scrotum and a chunk of flesh hanging loose on my inside leg bore painful witness to the pit bull's friendliness.

I thought I'd better ring my wife and break the bad news. I bought an *Echo* to conceal the rip in my trousers, then dialled from the phone in the waiting room. 'Hello, love. Don't get frightened, but I'm in Walton Hospital. I've been bitten by a dog.'

She sounded quite concerned. 'Whereabouts?'

'In Bootle, just by the Richmond Sausage factory.'

She burst out laughing. 'No, you twit! Whereabouts on your body?'

I glanced around cautiously to make sure I couldn't be overheard. Big Ron was due in sometime with his varicose veins and, besides, walls had ears. You couldn't be too careful. Those sods I worked with had their spies everywhere. They were bound to find out eventually, but there was no point handing it to them on a plate.

I lowered my voice to a whisper. 'On my... er... you know... middle stump.'

She was silent for a moment as she tried to figure out the coded message. Then she burst out laughing. I slammed the phone down, disgusted. So much for wifely tenderness! I'd come within a millimetre of being the last of the Cowhig line and she could barely contain her hilarity.

I eased myself gently into a chair. If anything, the pain was getting worse. I hoped I would not have to wait too long for treatment.

There were about ten of us sitting round the room. Two, particularly, stood out. One was a wizened old man whose body erupted, every few seconds, into uncontrollable shakes; the other was a strange character, leaning forward with hands clasped firmly together, muttering softly to himself under his breath. I assumed he was praying towards Mecca but I wasn't sure which one. The bingo hall in Norris Green was probably the nearest.

The religious man suddenly turned to the man on his left and whispered in his ear. The man shook his head emphatically. He turned and whispered to the man on his right. Again the response was a firm shake of the head. He leant his body even further forward and resumed his prayers.

Just then the dragon in uniform reappeared, carrying another piece of paper. Not more questions surely! What did she want to know this time? What kind of wallpaper I had in my lounge? But no. She walked across to the religious man who jumped up eagerly.

'Excuse me, nurse. Will I have to wait much longer?' he asked urgently.

'I don't know, sir. We're not ready for you yet.' Her voice carried no trace of sympathy.

'Oh, God!' He whispered something in her ear.

'Absolutely not!' She shook her head decisively and held out the paper in front of him. 'Do you know which of these it was?' The religious man said he didn't. 'Pity! Well, we'll see if we can find the right solvent but I can't say how long it'll take.' She walked briskly away.

The religious man could take it no longer. He raised his hands as if in supplication to heaven. 'Oh, God! I can't wait any longer. I'm desperate to go to the toilet but I can't go on my own.' He looked round in appeal, then realised some explanation was necessary. 'I've superglued my hands together. Will anyone help?'

We all tried hard to avoid catching his eye, except for one man who nodded assent. Since this was the man with the shakes, his reaction was probably involuntary, but the religious man was in no position to be choosy.

'Thank you, thank you! You've saved my life,' he said effusively, levering up his saviour with his arms and propelling him towards the toilet.

The man who'd been sitting on his left was less confident. 'I wouldn't be too sure. Judging by the state of that poor fellow, they'll be in there all day.'

I never did find out how long they took. At that moment the nurse came back in and called my name. The other patients looked on enviously as I followed her up the corridor and into a little room.

'Take your shoes and trousers off and lie down. Doctor Rees will be with you in a moment.'

I did as requested, very slowly, and lay down on the examination table. I reckoned I'd be off work for at least two weeks. And then the jokes would begin: endless renditions of Colonel Bogey, a vote to find me a new (girl's) name, frilly knickers left around the locker room. It was bad enough when Mogsy had had a vasectomy. With my injury I had no chance.

And yet...! I felt a sudden flicker of hope. Why would they have to know? I could say I'd fallen over and sprained an ankle or damaged a knee. That would explain the inevitable John Wayne walk. And my GP was a family friend so he wouldn't mind telling a little white lie on the sick note. Yes, it might work. There was no need for anyone at the depot to find out. My spirits rose.

'Hello there, boyo.' A young, florid-faced man with a booming Welsh voice entered the room. 'Doctor Rees at your service. Excuse me a moment.' He took out a toothpick from his pocket and prodded around ostentatiously in his mouth. 'That's better. I've just been chewing some nuts. Get stuck between your teeth, don't they?' He roared with laughter at his own joke. 'Now let's have a look at the scene of the crime.' He yanked my pants down past my knees.

I winced as he poked and prodded none too gently though he did his best to reassure me. 'You know the testicles are much stronger than people imagine. There's a man in China who can tie a rope to them and drag along an anvil.' I shuddered. In my present state it was not something on which to dwell.

'Only a little graze this, boyo,' he concluded giving one final squeeze. I yelped in pain and nearly fell off the table. 'You're very fortunate. I used to see far worse than this every week.'

'Really?' I was feeling far too sore to appreciate my good fortune.

'Oh, yes, I used to be club doctor for the Pontypridd rugby team, you know. I can remember Owen Williams getting his balls r-r-r-ipped off' – he sprayed me with saliva as he said this – 'during a grudge match against Swansea. Refused to go off for treatment. Had to stitch them back at half time, I did. Owen went straight back out and scored the winning try. He's got five children now and rides a bike twelve miles to work every day. Lots of cobbled streets in Wales too, boyo!'

He called for a nurse. It was not the grand inquisitor who appeared. This one was fit, fluffy and feminine. 'Clean up the wound, please, sweetie. I'll need to stitch it.'

'Of course, doctor. You know I'll do anything for you.' Her tone suggested their relationship went beyond the professional.

Doctor Rees turned his attention reluctantly back to me. 'Then there was the time Dai Roberts got a boot embedded in his scrotum. Friendly, it was. Pontypridd against Cardiff or was it Llanelli? Anyway, I had no equipment with me. Had to use the toolbox from my car. Couple of twists with a spanner, drop of oil, stick on a set of jump leads and he was as good as new. Kicked the winning penalty, you know.'

His healing touch, it transpired, was not limited to humans.

'Had a pet dog once. Silly sod pissed on a live cable and castrated himself. Fortunately it was round Christmas time so we had a bowl of walnuts in the house. Popped a couple in place, quick bit of embroidery and he was as happy as Larry. Fathered six litters of puppies and became supreme champion at Crufts. Honest, boyo.'

Every so often, he'd look over at the nurse who either giggled or smiled back coyly. I wondered if my presence was strictly necessary. I felt increasingly that I was playing gooseberry.

I gritted my teeth as the wound was sterilised. Then Doctor Rees picked up a needle. 'It's only a couple of tiny stitches. Don't want to bother with an anaesthetic do we?'

I assured him it would not be any bother.

'As you please.' His expression suggested that no Welsh rugby player would ever be so spineless.

'OK, you'll just feel a little prick.' I knew he'd get that one in somewhere. He gave me the local anaesthetic I'd so cravenly requested and began to put in the stitches. All the while he never stopped talking. This was, he explained, good medical practice to keep the patient's mind off his injury. So he told me about the Romans.

'The ancient Romans used to swear by their testicles,' he said. What the hell was he talking about now? 'Oh, yes. They used to hold their testicles whenever they swore an oath in court. Didn't have bibles, you see, so they had to find something equally precious.' He winked at the young nurse. 'Quite logical, I suppose. Anyway, that's where the word *testify* comes from.

'The Samurai warriors, now, they had a different trick. Before going into battle, they used to push their testicles back up into their bodies. Reduce the risk of injury – that's how we get the phrase *gird one's loins*.'

71

Doctor Rees was a veritable mine of useless information. I wondered if *Fascinating Facts About Testicles* had been required reading at medical school. Unfortunately his tactic was counter-productive. Not only did it fail to take my mind off the injury – it ensured I'd think about nothing else for days.

He finally finished and told me to get dressed. I slid off the table and bent down to pull up my pants.

'Oh, that reminds me,' said Doctor Rees. 'Don't move!' I felt something sharp rammed into my rear. 'I nearly forgot – tetanus injection.'

I stepped into my trousers and began to fasten them tentatively.

'Not planning a night of unbridled sexual bliss, are you, boyo?' Doctor Rees looked meaningfully at the young nurse who blushed. I confirmed that I wasn't. 'Good, I'd lay off sex for the next six hours if I were you. Give it a chance to settle down.' I thanked him for the treatment. 'Think nothing of it, boyo. I enjoyed it.' Somehow I didn't find that too hard to believe.

With difficulty, I reached down to put on my shoes.

'Let me do that.' Doctor Rees knelt down and tied my shoelaces. 'There you go.' He stood up, suddenly concerned. 'Look, I hope you didn't find my bedside manner too eccentric, did you?'

'Not at all,' I lied.

'Good. It's working in this madhouse that does it, you know. Dealing with too many oddballs.' His booming laugh echoed in my ears as I limped away down the corridor.

No sex for six hours! As if! Six days, six weeks, six years, maybe never, the way I was feeling at the moment. I'd had better days, I thought as I stood waiting for the bus home. And I'd received no sympathy. I thought of the humourless nurse and her interminable questions; her simpering colleague, more attentive to the doctor than to his patient; the wisecracking comic from the valleys, unhealthily obsessed with all things testicular; and worst of all, my own loving wife to whom the whole episode was one huge joke. And the bus was late!

When it did arrive, I couldn't believe it. There at the wheel was my caring driver. He was delighted to see me. 'Hello there, mate. How did you get on? Everything OK?'

'Could be worse,' I said automatically, settling into the same seat as before. And, on reflection, that much was true. I really ought to stop feeling sorry for myself and count my blessings. I was still very sore but at least I'd suffered no permanent damage. More importantly, Tommy and the others need never know the truth. I'd say a dog had chased me and I'd fallen down some steps. I'd put that in my accident report and no-one would be any the wiser. Yes, I was going to get away with it. Things weren't so bad after all.

'Good,' said the driver. 'No need for the sirens on this trip, then?'

'No, you can stop and pick up some passengers now.' We both laughed as he drove off.

For several minutes, we conversed pleasantly. It was easily my most civilised encounter of the day. We spoke about football, music, politics, art. We discovered we shared the same opinions, attitudes, tastes, interests; and we both had the misfortune to support Everton. I thought I'd found a true soul mate.

Eventually, we stopped outside the Mecca Bingo in Norris Green. About twenty women were waiting and they all piled on. A large lady, with a face like a bulldog chewing a wasp, brought up the rear.

Suddenly, I felt a tap on my shoulder. 'Hello, Dave, you're working late. Where've you been?'

I froze as I looked up into the kindly features of Mogsy's mother. God! She was a lovely woman but she couldn't keep a secret if her life depended on it. She could

gossip for England. Still, there was no need to panic. The newspaper was firmly in place on my lap.

'Er, hello, Mrs Morris.' I knew the drill. Keep as close to the truth as possible. 'I've been up to Walton Hospital. Fell down a flight of steps. Hurt my leg quite badly. Think I'm going to be off work for a bit.'

She sat down behind me. 'Oh, that's a shame. I'll tell our Steve when I get in.' That suited me fine. By the time I returned to work, the lie would be firmly established. I was safe. I began to feel quite smug.

Meanwhile the woman chewing the wasp was haranguing the driver. 'Over three quarters of an hour I've been waiting! Where the bleedin' hell have you been?'

My new friend, well versed in the skills of customer care, kept calm. 'I'm very sorry, madam, but two buses have broken down. I do apologise for your inconvenience.'

His diplomacy was in vain. She would not be mollified. 'You're sorry? How do you think I feel? It's an absolute disgrace!'

Mrs Morris leant forward and whispered in my ear. 'She's got a right cob on. She was sweating on one number for a thousand pounds. Never came up.'

The woman's fury showed no sign of abating. 'What's your number? I'm reporting you. I know what you lot are like. Sixty minute tea breaks! Two hours for lunch! On strike at the drop of a hat! You fellows are all the same!'

The driver remained unruffled, at least outwardly. 'You're quite at liberty to write to the management, madam, but, as I've already explained, two buses have broken down. This one is actually on time. Now, may I have your fare, please?'

She wasn't listening. 'You couldn't care less about the general public. I'm not putting up with this. You've not heard the end of it.'

The driver continued to show great self-restraint but she kept on and on and on. I could see the veins on his temple throbbing as he struggled to control his anger. Finally he snapped. He stood up, drew himself to his full height and looked her straight in the eye.

'Will you stop your infernal complaining? You think you've been hard done by?' He thrust a trembling forefinger in my direction. 'See this poor bastard here?' All eyes on the bus focused on me curiously. 'You don't hear him complaining, do you?' I knew what he was going to say and tried to shrink inconspicuously into my seat. Behind me Mrs Morris listened intently. 'No!' he went on as unstoppable as the Flying Scotsman. 'And he's on his way back from Walton Hospital. Just had his balls chewed off by a pit bull!'

THE LOVE BOAT

For many years Sefton Park had the best boating lake in Liverpool with twenty boats, all painted in bright, bold colours. Back in the late sixties this number was reduced to nineteen. I'm one of the few people to know what happened to the twentieth boat.

In 1873 Edward Simpson, a wealthy local wine merchant, built Ashdale House overlooking Sefton Park. Incorporated into the plans for the house was the biggest private wine cellar in Liverpool, measuring more than four thousand square feet. Edward used to host lavish parties for the city's professional classes and one can only imagine how many hangovers his wine created. But time, alas, changes everything. On the day I called to the house there was very little wine in the cellar – but there were several thousand gallons of water.

I walked up the secluded driveway taking in the faded grandeur of the big old house. Paint was peeling from the rotted woodwork, windows were cracked and the classical stone columns by the entrance were crumbling badly. On the front door was a huge lion's head knocker, encrusted with rust, which creaked protestingly as I seized it to announce my arrival. While I stood waiting I remembered Tommy's advice – 'Better watch yourself, there's a couple of rear gunners live there.' I half-expected the door to be opened by an ex-RAF officer with a clipped accent and a Ronald Colman moustache. What I did not expect was a man with shoulder-length silver hair, a black velvet cap and a crimson smoking jacket. He greeted me like an old friend.

'What a nice surprise!' He took my hand and shook it warmly. 'Do come in, dear boy. So kind of you to remember. Jerome and I get so few visitors these days.' He stepped aside and ushered me through into the entrance hall. 'Please make yourself at home. Incidentally, who are you?'

'I'm the Lecky Man,' I managed to say finally. 'I've come to empty your meter.' I couldn't take my eyes off his face. He was older than my dad and wearing full make-up with blue eyelids and lips as glossy as Kathy Kirby's. This may have been the swinging sixties, but I was a callow youth of eighteen and I'd never seen anything like it before.

'Excellent! I thought for a moment you might have been one of those religious chappies. You know, the ones who won't take no for an answer.'

'I knew a sailor in Portsmouth who wouldn't take no for an answer,' called a voice from over his shoulder. A hand appeared and took my own limply. 'Pleased to meet you.' Its owner moved into view and winked at me. It was just like queuing for a bus. I'd waited eighteen years to see a man wearing make-up and then two of them came along together.

The man with silver hair gestured toward his companion. 'May I introduce my fellow artiste, Jerome. I ' – he pronounced the word sonorously – 'am Homer.'

Jerome looked quite a bit younger than Homer and was a couple of inches taller. He wore only a hint of make-up, but looked equally flamboyant in a blue and white striped jacket and cream trousers, which set off nicely his peroxide hair. Both men sported silk cravats beneath their collars.

'This charming young man has offered to empty our electricity meter,' Homer explained. 'What do you think?'

'Ooh, yes,' Jerome replied. 'We don't want our slot getting jammed, do we?'

'It may break the monotony of dullness which blights our miserable existence.' Homer paused. 'Very different from our days treading the boards, of course,' he added deliberately.

'Oh, are you on the stage, then?' From his manner and appearance, I could never have guessed!

'Not are, dear boy, were. Before retirement was thrust upon us.'

'Really! What exactly did you do?' I asked. 'Were you actors?'

'We were professional variety entertainers,' Homer announced grandly.

I was immediately interested. My parents had been big fans of the old music hall. 'That must have been a really fascinating life.'

'Kept the wolf from the door,' Homer replied nonchalantly. 'There may be the odd memento lying around somewhere, if you're interested.' He made a vague gesture with his arm. 'Ah yes.' He pushed open the door of the drawing room. 'You may care to look around while Jerome makes the necessary preparations.' As Jerome stepped daintily along the hall, I followed Homer into the room. The 'odd memento' caught my eye at once. All four walls were covered entirely by rows of framed posters.

'From the halcyon days of yesteryear. Souvenirs of our great and glorious past. Before the applause of the crowd fell eternally silent.'

I scanned the posters eagerly.

LIVERPOOL'S GAY TROUBADOURS
HOMER AND JEROME.
THEY'LL KEEP YOU IN THE PINK
WITH A GIGGLE AND A WINK

They'd appeared all over the country, usually well down the bill, supporting all kinds of acts: Dewsbury Empire, 1946, supporting Albert Modley; Hippodrome Goole, 1948, supporting Harold Ecklethorp; Palace Theatre Halifax, 1949, supporting Dabber Davies; Vaudeville Barrow, 1950, supporting Gwendolen Graham; Grand Theatre Brighton, 1952, supporting Earle and Vaughan; and countless others. They'd even topped the bill once, at the Elysium Theatre, Scunthorpe, supported by, amongst others, Charmer, the world-famous counting horse (whatever did happen to him?)

Homer pointed to one of the posters – Bijou Workington, 1958 – where they were fourth on the bill below The Magical Marvo.

'This was the last time the world saw us. First house on a Friday. Jerome dried up halfway through the act and just ran off the stage. We'd had a couple of criminally unfair reviews and the poor boy's confidence was totally drained. He couldn't take it any more. A lot of the traditional venues were closing down anyway, so we chose to retire from the profession in our prime. I have some private means – a mere pittance, in truth – so we shut ourselves away in this tiny shack to lick our wounds.'

I wasn't too sure about the shack – the house must have had twenty rooms at a conservative estimate – but I made the right sympathetic noises. 'That's a shame. I suppose you can't please everyone though.'

'Such is the lot of all artistes, I'm afraid. Malicious critics, the uneducated rabble that passes for an audience. We are forever profaned by the scorn of the envious and the ignorant.'

Homer's lamentations were interrupted by the sound of Jerome's voice echoing faintly below. 'Everything's ready.'

'Don't say anything to Jerome,' Homer warned. 'He's still a bit sensitive. Doesn't like to be reminded. Follow me.' He led the way along the hall towards the back of the house where a flight of stone steps led down to the cellar. I followed him down, then stopped in amazement.

I blinked hard and looked again. The cellar, illuminated by rows of twinkling fairy lights strung up on the ceiling, was under several feet of water. At the bottom of the steps stood Jerome alongside a small rowing boat. The whole scene looked like a cross between Santa's grotto and a fairground tunnel of love.

'We've had a bit of a leak,' Homer explained. 'Rather unfortunate. Those petty bureaucrats at the water board said it was our responsibility to pump it out. Would you believe it?' He threw out his hands in a gesture of incredulity. 'Put it in the hands of our solicitor, Jerome said, didn't you, dear boy?'

'Ooh, yes! I put something in the hands of a solicitor once, didn't I? Great fun! Mind you, I'd had a few drinks first.' I wasn't sure how to react. Homer was a bit fruity but Jerome was so camp he made Larry Grayson look like a cold-eyed killer from the SAS.

Homer took up the story again. 'Nearly three months we've had to put up with it. Good thing those dear boys in the park were so helpful in getting us the boat. It's the only way we can put money in the meter.' He looked me up and down. 'Hmm, can you swim, dear boy?' I had to confess that I couldn't. 'You'd better wear this then.' He took a life-jacket from a peg on the wall and handed it to me. Any confidence this gave me was quickly nullified by the letters *SS Titanic* stencilled

VAUDEVILLE THEATRE
BARROW

WEEK COMMENCING MONDAY 26 JUNE 1950.
TWO PERFORMANCES NIGHTLY
PRICES: 2/-, 3/-, 4/-, SATURDAY NIGHT ONLY 3/-, 4/-, 5/-,

VARIETY FANFARE
A COCKTAIL OF MIRTH, MELODY AND MYSTERY

VOICE FROM THE VALLEYS

GWENDOLEN GRAHAM
THE RHONDDA NIGHTINGALE

ORIENTAL MYSTERY FROM ## THE GREAT NAKAJIMA INSCRUTABLE JAPANESE MAGICIAN	SPLIT YOUR SIDES WITH ## SID SOWERBUTTS. THE CHAP WITH THE CAP
OLD FAVOURITES SUNG BY ## PATRICK O'REILLY HE'S A BROTH OF A BOY	KNIFE THROWER ## AUSTIN SHEFFIELD IS THERE A DOCTOR IN THE HOUSE?
A GIGGLE AND A WINK ## HOMER AND JEROME LIVERPOOL'S GAY TROUBADOURS	## THE CARLOTTA SISTERS WHIRLWIND ROLLER SKATERS
THE MOLLY MITCHELL DANCERS BARROW'S VERY OWN	THE AMAZING DUPONTS YOUNG EQUILIBRISTS

AT THE ORGAN – JANET HARTLES

78

on the back. 'We're both very strong swimmers. I do the crawl but Jerome can only manage the doggy paddle.'

'That's not quite true,' Jerome corrected him. 'I can do the breast stroke but I am happier doing it doggy style.'

Homer let me climb aboard, then got in and sat beside me. Jerome untethered the boat from its mooring – a solid iron ring conveniently embedded in the cellar wall – and stood for several seconds with twelve inches of rope dangling limply from his hand. His face registered the most intense dismay.

'Must be the cold weather,' he concluded, shrugging his shoulders. He stepped into the boat.

'Now, punt!' said Homer looking up at him.

Jerome pouted in annoyance. 'No need to be insulting... oh, I see what you mean.' He looked towards a punt pole resting across two large hooks in the wall. He reached for it and eyed its dimensions admiringly.

Homer gestured towards the far end of the cellar. 'Are we all ready? Then lead on, Macduff.'

We set off down a narrow central passageway. On either side foundation walls divided the cellar into little rooms or alcoves, joined to the central aisle and each other by a series of interconnecting archways. The meter was about eighty feet away at the front of the house. When the city was electrified around 1920, all meters were placed at the nearest access point to the outside main, in order to economise on cable. The planners could not have foreseen that, in this particular house, you'd need a cross-channel expedition to reach it.

'O sole mio...' The first verse of *The Gondoliers Song* echoed round the cellar. Despite my suspicion that I was alone with two certifiable lunatics, I was impressed by the melodious quality of their voices as they serenaded one another.

As we passed the first alcove, I was totally disoriented. Everything seemed so unreal. Looking at the two men, their made-up faces glistening in the eerie light, I felt like an extra in Herbert Lom's *Phantom of the Opera*.

By the time they'd finished the song, we'd reached the other end of the cellar. Cautiously I stood up, trying not to unbalance the boat, then unlocked the meter, emptied it and counted the money. I carefully replaced the box and handed the divvy to Homer. His gratitude was so effusive you'd think I'd presented him with a cheque for a million pounds.

He clapped me on the shoulder. 'Thank you so much, dear boy. Jerome, we have wealth beyond our wildest dreams. I suggest a holiday. What do you say?'

Jerome reflected for a moment. 'I'm game,' he said, 'but then I always am.'

'We will treat our most generous benefactor to a world cruise,' Homer announced. 'It's the least we can do. Are you, by any chance, widely travelled?' he asked me. I supposed tramping the streets of Liverpool didn't count. 'Well then,' he assured me, 'you're in for a treat.'

Jerome began to punt back up the cellar, then turned right under one of the arches.

Suddenly Homer pointed dramatically. 'Look, Mount McKinley!'

'Don't mind if I do,' said Jerome under his breath.

I followed the direction of Homer's finger and saw a poster for **Alaska** on the wall.

'I climbed that mountain once,' Jerome continued, 'but I got into difficulties.'

'Really?' asked Homer on cue.

'Yes, I was stuck on a very narrow ledge and I couldn't go up or down. It was terrible. Had to send up the distress flares.'

'How awful, dear boy! You must have been very frightened.'

'Yes, I was clinging on in panic. Didn't dare move.'

'Enough to put you off for life.'

'Ooh, I don't know. All turned out happily in the end.'

'Glad to hear it, dear boy. What happened?'

Jerome smiled slyly. 'They sent out a nice young mountaineer to rescue me. He came and pulled me off.'

Jerome continued to steer in and out of the different rooms, all of which were liberally adorned with travel posters. Each room, it seemed, represented a different part of the world. We must have circumnavigated the globe two or three times and every so often a poster would trigger happy reminiscences;

Canada – 'Jerome wanted to join the Mounties. They always get their man.'

Isle of Wight – 'It's especially lovely in Cowes week. Lots of nice buoys floating round.'

Australia – 'Homer's still very big down under.'

Isle of Man – 'We both had the time of our lives in Douglas.'

Just after we left **Prague** – 'Beautiful city. Wonderful cathedral with a particularly fine organ' – Homer clapped his hand against his head. 'Jerome, dear boy, what are we doing? We have invited this young gentleman on a cruise but have neglected to supply refreshment. It's scandalous.'

Jerome nodded gravely. 'You're right, Homer. Where are our manners?'

'What is a cruise without refreshment? We have been terribly remiss.' Homer reached under the seat with his hand. 'Hello, what's this?' he said in a tone of the greatest surprise, pulling out a bottle of the finest port. 'By Jove! What a tremendous piece of good fortune! For once that harlot, fate, has smiled upon us.' He reached under again and brought out three wine glasses. 'I assume this craft is licensed.' Jerome nodded. 'Then I propose we drop anchor here awhile. The sea is pleasantly calm. Jerome, would you be so good as to attend to the beverages?'

Jerome gently lay down the punt pole and carried out his task.

The lights shimmered softly on the water as we sat and sipped the port in companionable silence. I was beginning to warm to this odd couple, but still Homer's brow was furrowed. Things were not quite right.

Eventually he spoke. 'Something is yet amiss. Jerome, is it not also traditional for cruises to supply a modicum of entertainment?'

'I believe so.'

'Then what is that beneath your seat?' Jerome's hand emerged clutching a small suitcase. Homer opened it and sat back dumbfounded. 'Good heavens! I do believe it's a banjo! At last Dame Fortune has seen fit to compensate for her years of outrageous neglect.' He put down his glass and gestured to Jerome to pick up the banjo. 'In which case, I am proud to introduce, brought out of retirement by popular demand, Liverpool's Gay Troubadours, Homer and Jerome!'

The boat nearly capsized as they stood up and gave a little bow. Homer turned to his partner – 'Music, maestro,' – and they burst into song.

> *With a giggle and a wink,*
> *We'll put you in the pink,*
> *'Cause we're the boys to drive your blues away.*
> *No matter if you're fickle,*
> *Your fancy we will tickle,*
> *We'd like to make the whole world gay.*

Jerome sang the last two verses by himself.

> *I met a pretty girly,*
> *Who looked a little surly.*
> *I said, 'Let's go and have a little fun.'*
> *So I took her to the park,*
> *But after it got dark,*
> *I noticed that her buttons were undone.*

> *Now I thought I'd better tell 'er,*
> *I'm not that sort of feller,*
> *I'd rather have a nice stiff drink.*
> *But I was in a pickle,*
> *'Cause she wants slap and tickle,*
> *And all I want's a giggle and a wink.*

I laughed out loud and I wasn't just being polite. Jerome's air of exaggerated mock-innocence was so funny that I couldn't help myself.

Encouraged by my reaction, Homer turned to his partner. 'You know, Jerome, when we return from our cruise, we really should devote more time to our garden.'

'Ooh, yes, the early frost's been nipping at my sweet williams. Very painful.'

'I knew a fellow once who had extraordinarily green fingers.'

'Ooh, that's horrible!' Jerome grimaced. 'Why didn't he use a hanky?'

Homer ignored this. 'Very proud of his ferns, he was, especially the fronds. Anyway one day he decided he wanted to grow anemones. But the results were a disaster. He was extremely upset. He said, *you know, it's funny, my fronds are perfect but I just can't grow anemones.*' Homer leant over towards me. 'So do you know what I told him, dear boy?'

I shook my head.

'I told him not to worry. With fronds like that, who needs anemones?'

'I prefer pansies myself,' said Jerome.

'Be that as it may.' Homer held out his hand. 'Do you mind if I play upon your instrument, dear boy?'

Jerome rolled his eyes suggestively. 'I don't if you don't.' He passed over the banjo.

'Thank you so much. Most kind.'

'Think nothing of it. The pleasure's mine.'

This time Homer played the banjo while Jerome sang the whole song on his own.

There was a chap I know,
Who was looking rather low,
So I took him home and offered him some wine.
As he poured some in his cup,
I said, 'Bottoms up.'
He said, 'Thank you.' I said, 'No, the pleasure's mine.'

While fishing one fine day,
I heard a young man say,
'There's something pulling hard upon my line.'
I said, 'That's huge, by God!
Shall I help you hold your rod?'
He said, 'Thank you.' I said, 'No, the pleasure's mine.'

A friend who'd an ambition
To be a great musician
Lost his trumpet and began to pine.
I said, 'Don't despair, old fruit,
You may blow upon my flute.'
He said, 'Thank you.' I said, 'No, the pleasure's mine.'

I was laughing all through the song and, when it finished, applauded loudly.

Jerome really did have a pleasant light tenor voice and a wonderful range of facial expression. He seemed so naturally confident that it was hard to imagine him ever running off stage.

Homer told two more jokes. Both had cobwebs on when Noah first set sail on an earlier flood.

'Let's do another song,' suggested Homer, strumming a couple of chords on the banjo.

Jerome looked very doubtful.

'What's the matter, dear boy?'

'I don't like your plucking.'

'Never had any complaints before,' protested Homer, looking hurt.

Unmoved, Jerome reached for the banjo. 'I would prefer to do the whole performance on my own, thank you.'

Homer passed over the instrument ungraciously. 'Very well then, Jerome. Please yourself.'

'I always do. Which, of course, is why...

I'm still fancy free,
It's still I, not we.
Maybe I've been left upon the shelf.
But I don't care if fate
Deprives me of a mate.
I'm happy just to please myself.

Why worry unduly
If I satisfy yours truly?
I'm sure it can't be bad for my health.
It can be so much fun
Looking after number one
So I'm happy just to please myself.

I can't go to great expense,
My pocket's not immense,
I'm not a man of riches or great wealth.
But who needs to entertain
With caviare and champagne?
When I'm happy just to please myself.

Homer joined Jerome as he sang the final verse once more. At the end I again applauded heartily. I would have given them a standing ovation but didn't want to risk upsetting the boat.

'Too, too kind,' murmured Homer with obvious insincerity. Homer doffed his cap and they both winked, bowed twice and sat down. By now I was well behind on my daily schedule but I was in no hurry to go ashore. These two men had caught my imagination and I wanted to know more about them.

'Did you two perform together for long?' I asked.

'Ooh, cheeky!' said Jerome.

'I say, dear boy, we have only just met,' protested Homer.

I rephrased the question.

'Twelve years we did. Started up after the war. Theatres, cinemas, seaside piers, we've played them all. Sad to see the old variety dying out.'

'Oh yes,' said Jerome, arching an eyebrow. 'I like a bit of variety.'

'Yes, indeed. I miss the old music halls. We shall not see their like again. Such wonderful old buildings, too. Not like these modern monstrosities.'

I had to agree. I didn't much care for sixties architecture.

Nor, it seemed, did Jerome. 'Ooh, I know! Erections today aren't what they used to be!'

I was curious to know how they had developed their act over the years. Again I worded the question badly.

'You know when you first started out in variety...'

'Yes, dear boy.'

'... was one of you an ordinary straight man?'

'Not our style at all,' retorted Jerome instantly.

Homer was quite indignant. 'Really, dear boy, your prurience is becoming intolerable!'

I tried a new tack. 'Did you ever appear locally?' I asked. 'My mum and dad might have seen you.'

'We were national performers,' said Homer importantly, 'but sometimes public clamour enticed us back to our native shores. The Shakespeare Theatre and Lodge Lane Pavilion, to be precise.'

Jerome hung his head in shame. 'Ooh, the Pivvy! Don't mention that place! I've never felt so humiliated.'

By now I should have known better but I took the bait. 'Why, what happened?'

'Scene of a highly embarrassing incident with one of the other artistes,' said Homer in the gravest of tones. 'Poor Jerome had an unfortunate misunderstanding with the sword swallower. We never could go back.'

'Well, I didn't know!' Jerome's face took on a deeply pained expression and, though it was hard to tell in the eerie glow, I could have sworn he was blushing. 'Pleasant young chap he was, too. I was most disappointed.'

'It's a pity you had to retire so early,' I said. 'Couldn't you have tried something else?' Then I remembered Jerome's loss of confidence and wondered if I was intruding into something he would rather forget.

There was an awkward silence before Homer stepped in. 'Awfully difficult to find something for artistes of our cal-eye-bre.' The last word had the second syllable accentuated in true theatrical style. 'And of course, we were known as variety specialists.'

'Mind you,' said Jerome, not at all abashed, 'Homer did once display his Willy before the masses.' He paused for effect. 'Quite a big part, it was too.'

I blinked hard. An image began to form in my mind. I tried to banish it quickly.

'Yes, indeed. I have dabbled with the Bard in my time. Played in *A Midsummer Night's Dream* wearing an ass's head, would you believe? Did rather limit my nuances of interpretation.'

'Ah!' I'd read the play at school so I saw this one coming. 'I know, they didn't like your Bottom.'

Homer was silent for several seconds.

'No,' he intoned deeply, 'they didn't. Said I had insufficient stage presence.' His mouth quivered. 'What an insult! Can you believe that? Me! Insufficient stage presence! O judgement, thou art fled to brutish beasts, and men have lost their reason.'

At first I assumed he was still acting. The boat swayed as he rose to his feet. 'Life's but a walking shadow, a poor player, that struts and frets his hour upon the stage...' – his voice faltered and his shoulders seemed to visibly sag – '. . . full of sound and fury... signifying...' – he slumped back onto his seat, staring vacantly ahead – '... absolutely bloody sod all!'

Tears welled up in Homer's eyes and began to trickle down his cheeks. 'Critics! What do they know about it, anyway? Philistines! Parasites! They chew a man's soul into tiny pieces and spit it out into the dust!' He buried his face in his hands, sobbing loudly.

Jerome put his arm round his friend's shoulders. 'It's alright, Homer, don't worry about it. I'll take you home.'

We headed straight back to the cellar steps, sailing directly past South America, New Zealand and Hong Kong. Homer stayed slumped in his seat as I removed the life-jacket and climbed ashore.

Jerome tied up the boat and helped him out. 'Come on. You go and have a lie-down.' He guided Homer up the steps and back into the house.

'I'm sorry about Homer. He'll be alright when you've gone. You know what delicate sensibilities we performers have.' There was a distinct element of self-mockery in Jerome's tone. We were standing in the hall. Homer was reclining on a chaise-longue (what else?) in the drawing room, consoling himself with the rest of the port. He had insisted on showing me his old, yellowed cuttings, though these had only exacerbated his distress. He couldn't leave it alone.

Some of the reviews had been very cruel:

A giggle and a wink? More like a groan and a yawn!

This appalling act should go far – the farther the better!

Unadulterated smut! The pleasure certainly wasn't mine!

*Variety is already dying! Tasteless routines like this
will hasten it to its grave.*

To call this act third rate would be an unforgivable exaggeration!

Others were more measured, but equally hurtful. One, not untypical, said:

*Though their material is unacceptably suggestive, the younger
man does possess charm and undeniable
comic potential. His partner's contribution is less clearly
defined, unless it is merely to carry the banjo. Maybe
Jerome really should look after number one and go solo.*

I couldn't get over the transformation in Jerome. He had dropped his campness entirely and seemed a different person.

'You see, it all meant so much to Homer. He loved performing. The stage was his whole life.'

'But I thought your act was very good. I enjoyed it, honestly.' This was the absolute truth. I'd been royally entertained in that cellar.

'Well, you're one of the few, but thank you anyway.'

'Why couldn't you have carried on? I mean, even if the music halls were closing down, there must have been other opportunities – TV, radio, holiday camps. What about the working men's clubs?'

Jerome laughed. 'My God! Can you imagine us at working men's clubs? No, I don't think so. And we were far too risqué for holiday camps. Most of the theatres thought we were way over the top, as it was, so we'd have had no chance. Besides – let's be honest – we were never really very good.'

I still thought he was underselling himself. 'But you're so versatile. You can sing and play the banjo and you're funnier than a lot of people on the telly. Did you never consider doing a solo act?'

Jerome shook his head. 'No. How could I? What would Homer have done? He would never have survived on his own.'

I thought I already knew the answer, but I asked the question anyway. 'What really happened the night you retired?'

Jerome smiled ruefully. 'It was terrible. The local press had hammered us – as usual – and the audience was baying for blood. Kept booing and chucking rotten tomatoes. Anyway, we got halfway through the act and Homer just snapped. Broke down crying – like today – and ran off stage. It was one rejection too many, I suppose. I could never have given him another. He would have been destroyed.'

'Suppose I'd better be on my way then,' I said finally. Jerome opened the front door for me. 'Well, goodbye then.'

'Goodbye.' Jerome shook my hand firmly.

'Thanks for the cabaret. And don't take any notice of the bad reviews. Maybe you were just too far ahead of your time.'

'Yes, maybe we were. It would be nice to think that. Take care.' He closed the front door. I was twenty feet away when it opened again. 'Oh, I nearly forgot.' I turned round and saw him give a great theatrical bow. 'Thank you for being such a wonderful audience.'

As I walked back down the driveway, an evil suspicion began to crystallise in my mind. I thought of the mooring ring embedded in the wall and the hooks for the punt pole and the fairy lights strung up on the ceiling. And I began to wonder. Had there really been a leak in the cellar or was it possible that Liverpool's Gay Troubadours had deliberately flooded it for their own amusement? I couldn't be sure but, whichever it was, I didn't really mind. I was just grateful that, for forty-five unforgettable minutes, I'd had my little cruise and Homer had had his stage.